COSMIC!

LIVERPOOL

Edited by Michelle Warrington

First published in Great Britain in 1999 by
POETRY NOW YOUNG WRITERS
1-2 Wainman Road, Woodston,
Peterborough, PE2 7BU
Telephone (01733) 230748
.

HB ISBN 0 75430 181 8
SB ISBN 0 75430 182 6

FOREWORD

With over 63,000 entries for this year's Cosmic competition, it has proved to be our most demanding editing year to date.

We were, however, helped immensely by the fantastic standard of entries we received, and, on behalf of the Young Writers team, thank you.

The Cosmic series is a tremendous reflection on the writing abilities of 8-11 year old children, and the teachers who have encouraged them must take a great deal of credit.

We hope that you enjoy reading *Cosmic Liverpool* and that you are impressed with the variety of poems and style with which they are written, giving an insight into the minds of young children and what they think about the world today.

CONTENTS

Holy Family RC Primary School

Joseph Ryan	34
Kayleigh Keane	35
Cheryl Gallagher	35
Melissa McConville	36
Eileen Powell	36
Brendan Thompson	37
Michael Hepworth	37
Craig O'Brien	38
Becky Thompson	38
Ashley Culvin	39
Gemma Scattergood	39
Sean Kennerley	40
Daniel Fox	40
Ceara Watson	41
Jennifer Reay	41
Emma Jones	42
Hayley Clarke	42
Joanne Parry	43
Therese Melvin	43
Anna Kyle	44

Holy Name JMI School

Rebecca Goldstein	44
Stephanie Kewley	45
Simba Muzavazi	46
Alex Gough	46
Natalie McCormick	46
David Gallagher	47
Jenni Callaghan	47
Carla English	48
Thomas Roberts	48
Alex Ashton	49
Catherine Jones	49
Francis Fearon	50
Natalie Hill	50
Natalie Palmer	51
Megan Fergus	51

Mackets CP School

Jenna Burden	52
Thomas McNiven	52
Diane Reeves	53
Shelly Duggan	54
Kate Holly Brown	54
Philip David Jameson	55
Kate Sutton	56
Marc Robinson	56
Robert Segar	56
John Coffey	57
Kayleigh Large	57
Melissa Ryan	57
Christian Ryan	58
Stephanie Calveley	58
Philip Soo	58
Sarah Jane Cartwright	59
Scott Holt	59
David Pownall	60
Jenny Johnson	60
Katie Baker	61
Philip Cliff	61
Michael Soo	62
Leanne Gault	62
Rachael Quayle	63
Natalie McDonald	63
Stevi Chapman	64
Mark Wheatley	64
Hayley Walker	65

Norman Pannell School

Gemma Murphy	65
Caroline Hampson	66
Allyce Midghall	66
Helen McKenna	67
Kate Stulberg	67
Karl Rawlinson	68
Kelly Corrin	68

Kayleigh Griffith	69
Clare Lawrence	69
Debbie Sanderson	70

Palmerston School

Mark Molyneaux	70
Michael Price	71

St Andrew's RC Primary School

Leanne Byrne	71
Lauren Hansen	72
Damon Daniels	72
Laura Atkinson	73
Natalie Goulding	74
Hayley Potter	74
David Barton-Cowley	75
Hayley Rignall	76
Alex Walpole	76
Andrea Jackson	77
Andrew Smith	77
Helen Jacobsen	78
Victoria Scahill	78
Paul George	79
Elizabeth Cousins	79
Tami Harper	80
Chantelle Kerrigan	80
Helen Range	81
John Moore	81
Suzanne Prescott	82
Joanne Griffiths	82
Lorna Duffy	83
Daniel O'Neill	83
Sara Mahamy	84
Matthew Cawley	84
Sarah Martin	85

St Cuthbert's JMI School

Kaylea Allport	85
Joel Canavan	86
Nina Orr	86
Anjalee Carney	87
Jenny Morris	88
Sarah Harrison	89
John Tyson	89
Daniel Tracey	90
Rebecca Doody	90
Heather McCarthy	91
Kirsty Taylor	91
Symone Aryeetey	92
Peter Nodwell	92
Rachael Bradley	93
Phoebe Dinn	93
David Morris	94
Kathy Roche	94
Katie Fox	95
James Parry	95
Jenny Melia	96
Keil Patterson	96
Luke Baker	97

St Laurence's RC School

Hannah Stanley	97

St Margaret Mary's Junior School

Christopher Golding	97
Jessica Lundberg	98
Ryan J Beeley	99
Kylie Windle	100
Rachael Hawkins	100
Rebecca Achilles	101
Danielle Davey	101
Faye Silvano	102
Danielle Brennan	102
David Jackson	102

THE POEMS

POCKET MONEY

Every Saturday I get my pocket money.
I sometimes buy comics that are funny.
I like buying sweets, crisps, laces and chewing gum,
Which makes me have a funny feeling in my tum.
Occasionally I buy football stickers which
                    I swap with my friends.
Now and again I get extra spends,
When I do jobs for my mum, like doing the
                    dishes or cleaning her car.
My pocket money goes extra far.
I look forward to Saturdays more than any other day.
When my mum calls me in to say,
'Your pocket money, don't spend it all today.
Remember there are six more days.
Don't go mad with your money though,
enjoy your pocket money and have a nice day.'

Matthew Donnelly (10)
Bishop Martin CE School

SPRING

Daffodil leaves begin to grow.
Showers and rain begin to go.
Easter eggs are being bought.
Little bunnies are being taught
How to do things for themselves.
The Easter Bunny is coming around
Giving Easter eggs to be found.
Baby animals are being born.
Lambs, kids and calves without their horn.
Snowdrops and bluebells begin to appear
In the woods and parks that are quite near.
Springtime is a colourful season.
People visit the parks for this reason.
I love the spring because it's a busy season.

Anna Donnelly (8)
Bishop Martin CE School

FEELINGS

Every day of my week,
I write the name I dare not speak,
The girl with the hazelnut hair,
My beloved and my despair,
I'll never let my feelings go,
Her name is in my heart,
Ringing and ringing like a bell,
Till she moved house one day,
My heart was broken,
I have tears in my eyes,
As I say my goodbyes.

Mark Redmond (10)
Blackmoor Park Junior School

TEACHERS

They are kind and never make people sad
Although they sometimes go mad.
Some wear glasses perched on their nose
And they also tell people not to doze.
They tell you to be quiet
But they never do it themselves.
Sometimes they say you're good
When the next minute you fall in mud.
Sometimes I get shouted at
But I never cry
Because I'm not a baby
And anyway, people will call me a moaner.
Sometimes I don't know how to spell
Things like elephant and banana
But I just guess
And in the end I get into a mess.
When you have been naughty
Teachers keep you in
And if you've been naughty as can be
They might even throw you in the bin!

Nicola Wong (9)
Blackmoor Park Junior School

MY PARENTS

My parents are very jolly
Most of the time they are off their trolley
They like to eat beans from Aberdeen
They eat green gravy because their crazy.

Chloe Jones (10)
Blackmoor Park Junior School

THE SEASONS

Springtime.
The tweets of birds,
the trickle of streams,
everything is nice and fresh.
Springtime.

Summer.
Summer's dew,
and trees and flowers bloom,
the nice hot summer's days are here
to stay.
Summer.

Autumn.
The trees are bare
and the days go colder
the weather really starts
to change.
Autumn.

Winter.
It starts to snow
the gales are blowing
Saint Nicholas will soon be here.
Winter.

Peter Yarushin (10)
Blackmoor Park Junior School

How They Found Him

They found him in Brazil
They found him in China
They found him in an old Scottish diner.

They found him eating fish
They found him eating chips
They found him eating off an old green dish.

They found him sad
They found him happy
They found him really bad.

They found him in a town
They found him in a city
They found him sitting with much pity.

They found him in a cottage
They found him in a house
They found him speaking to the owner.

They found him using a comb
They found him on his way
They found him at home.

By reading this you can tell,
He can be *anywhere!*

Janine Rice (9)
Blackmoor Park Junior School

BOOKS

Books.
Books are exciting.
From Dickens to Blyton,
And scary books that frighten,
They're better than watching TV.

Books.
Books can be funny,
Books can be sad,
Books can be exciting
But not often bad.

Books.
Unlike TV
You can read them
Anywhere:
On the toilet,
In the bath
Or just sitting on the bottom stair.

Books.
Just remember this:
From Dickens to Blyton,
And scary books that frighten,
They're better than watching TV!

Alan Jones (9)
Blackmoor Park Junior School

THE ZOO

In the zoo you will find
All different kinds
Like monkeys, cheetahs, kangaroos
Sitting in a line,
There's sea lions
And penguins all about,
Remember the snakes
And tarantulas crawling around,
Lions and tigers
They're ruling the world
The birds and bears
Are screeching and growling
And the parrots talk to you
The wild cats are pouncing
And ready to eat.
It's nearly bedtime
And time to sleep
They've had a busy day
With calling and shouting
in their ears
But wait, there's someone new arrived
in the zoo.
Yes it's the baby
            elephant.

Amanda Hughes (9)
Blackmoor Park Junior School

THE NOISES ARE SCARY

When the floorboards creak
The door goes slam
The scratching noise just carries on.
You're by yourself
You're all alone
Then suddenly you hear a groan.
A moaning noise inside your head
It keeps echoing on
You think it's gone for a single moment
But then you hear it again.
You are already sweating, dribbling down your face
Then all of a sudden, darkness rules
As the night draws on.
At once it's silent
The only thing is the tick of the clock
You wish you were asleep but you can't get to sleep
The noise won't stop.
Until at last you scream and scream
It seems like hours but at last it's light.

David McKenna (10)
Blackmoor Park Junior School

BASKETBALL

I like basketball I can throw for miles
I have slam-dunked from quite a stretch
Because my arms have lots of might
I have hung from quite a height
But the weird thing is I'm not light.

Karl Humphreys (9)
Blackmoor Park Junior School

PEOPLE

Some people are happy
Some people are sad
Some people are thin
And some people are fat.

Some people are tiny
Some people are small
Some people are midgets
They're not very tall.

Some people like sport
Some people do not
Some people like eating
More than a lot.

Some people like pizza
Some people like chips
Some people like biscuits
Or chocolate dips.

Janine Gregson (10)
Blackmoor Park Junior School

SPRING

S pring is when plants grow
P lants, plants everywhere
R acing through the hot, hot air
I n the flowers children play
N obody will stay away
G irls and boys will play and play.

Emma Almond (10)
Blackmoor Park Junior School

JEALOUSY

Jealousy is maroon and red,
Spurting from the fire,
It's lightning striking to the ground
A twisted, deep, desire.

A red and orange burning fire,
In a Gothic tower,
Deeper and deeper gets the fire,
Its jealous, envious power.

A leafless tree on the hill,
In the howling storm,
The bits of leaf on the ground.
Jealousy is born.

All these feelings are about . . .

Jealousy!

Rachel Murray (9)
Blackmoor Park Junior School

WINTER

W inter is very cold
I n winter the sail begins to mould
N asty, nasty frost bites
T easing people with snowball fights
E verywhere I turn
R olling in the snow children go.

Jade Ayers (10)
Blackmoor Park Junior School

FEAR

Fear is terror lurking in the night.
Fear is horrifying.
Fear is your heart beating.
Fear is horrid eyes looking at you.
Fear is being horrified.
Fear is being scared all around.
Fear is running away from somebody.
Fear is creaking in the dark.
Fear is something crawling.
Fear is bad breath.
Fear is a feeling of lava pouring down your head.
Fear is like blood pouring from your heart.
Fear is hearing somebody bury your coffin.
Fear is like being executed.
Fear is a feeling that is not pleasant.
So this feeling fear, you sometimes have to be scared.

Vincent Hunt (10)
Blackmoor Park Junior School

WINTER

W inter is very cold
I n winter it is very icy
N ow the snow is falling
T ony and I played snowball fights
E veryone loves the snow
R olling down the hill I go.

Laura Higgs (10)
Blackmoor Park Junior School

FRIGHTENERS

You're in bed, just woken-up from a really scary dream.
It's dark, you hear the floorboards creak.
Then the clock strikes twelve,
A flash of lightning outside your window,
A breeze suddenly goes through you.
You feel like someone is watching you.
Then the window blows open and the curtains blow out.
You can see a figure standing in the doorway,
You can just make out the outline of a figure,
It's a girl, she's floating, and you can see through her.
It's a ghost, she comes closer.
I was just about to scream when . . .
It goes light, she disappears,
Everyone starts to wake-up,
While I just sit there feeling
In a way I have never felt before.

Helen Peet (10)
Blackmoor Park Junior School

WINTERTIME

W inter is very cold.
I n winter it is very frosty.
N ow I like the snowball fights.
T rying to hit people with snowballs.
E very day I get a shiver down my spine.
R olling snow into a snowman.

Rachael Martin (10)
Blackmoor Park Junior School

MY EMOTIONS

My emotions are red and black,
I feel cold
As if I was lost
In a deep forest
With a wolf nearby.
I'm shaking all over, my lips have all dried up.
My heart is pounding,
Faster than ever.
I saw the fierce wolf,
With slobber dripping
All over his slimy mouth.
I felt as if the world was going round.
My face went pale-white,
I was terrified.
These are my emotions.

Claire Hendrick (9)
Blackmoor Park Junior School

THE SIMPSONS

The Simpsons are my favourite 'toon'
Homer chases Bart around the room
Homer is bald and fat
He likes eating, he's good at that
While Marge has Maggie to feed
Lisa enjoys a really good read.

Gemma Burns (10)
Blackmoor Park Junior School

CRICKET

There was an unusual girl
Who had blonde curly hair
She loved tennis and lived in Wales
Everywhere she went, she told tales
She hurt her head on some rails
I think that she is really tall
No one is really tall at all
She once entered a competition
She hit someone's head when playing cricket
She had to take her to the hospital
With a big, red head
She won the competition
The person was really sad
She won a big gold medal
With a big gold badge.

Louise Kinsella (10)
Blackmoor Park Junior School

WET WEEKENDS ARE BORING YOU CAN'T GO OUT

Wet weekends are boring
You can't go out
You stay inside, bored
You sit on the couch looking out of the window
At the rain thinking it is boring
It is better playing in the snow
You can have a snowball fight.

Laura Matthews (9)
Blackmoor Park Junior School

DISASTERS

'Oh you spoon' said my friend
As I hit the ball
And watched it bend
And hit the car and smashed a window
Hit Mr Bradly's head
And into the garden
'Oh no' my friend said
'We're dead'
I dashed inside to hide
I ran through the kitchen
Pots and pans fly
I hide
I don't go out for two hours
But when I did there was murder
Real murder.

Jack Robinson (10)
Blackmoor Park Junior School

MY SISTER HEATHER

Heather, Heather is the best.
She is better than the rest.
She has got very beautiful hair.
Her favourite fruit is a big juicy pear.
She has got a little pink nose.
And I really love her loads.
I'm really glad that she's my sister.

Juliet Parr (9)
Blackmoor Park Junior School

MOUSE

My pet cat was called Mouse,
He liked to venture around the house,
Until one day I have to say,
Poor Mouse got torn away.

I knew sooner or later
I would not have to buy any fish,
Because that was his favourite dish.

That day that he died,
I just had to cry
But Mum said 'Hold it in.'

I was full of fear,
When I wiped away a tear,
I'll never see poor Mouse again.

Caroline Waters (10)
Blackmoor Park Junior School

THE SUN

The sun is nice it shines so bright
On the summer morning.
The birds come out and shout out loud
'What a lovely morning.'
It is so hot your skin turns red
It itches so much you go crazy.
You wake up with a tan
And that's why the sun is fab.

Melissa Knipe (9)
Blackmoor Park Junior School

SPORTS

I love sports,
I play football, cricket and tennis,
Because I love these sports.
I play all day and I play all night,
Usually it ends up in a fight,
We walk away and do not play,
Until the next day comes.
I go away,
I can't play without one of my friends.
And I get really bored after a while,
So I go in my room,
Until we play again.
I'd miss school for sports,
Because I love sports.

Sean Evans (10)
Blackmoor Park Junior School

LET'S GO ON A WET WALK

Let's go on a wet walk
Let's go on a wet walk
See the puddles, see them grow
Here is a big one, in we go
A rainbow, red, orange, yellow, green, blue, indigo,
and violet.
The biggest rainbow we have ever seen
We went on a wet walk.

Christopher Munro (9)
Blackmoor Park Junior School

THOUGHTS IN MY MIND

As I lie in my bed,
With thoughts in my head,
I think of the world around us,
The daffodils, the bees,
And blossoming trees,
Are all so beautiful,
The sky is so blue,
As we can see,
The sun is hot,
As hot as can be,
The white, fluffy clouds,
Go floating by,
As soft gentle raindrops,
Fall from the sky.

Lianne Ferguson (10)
Blackmoor Park Junior School

ANIMALS IN DANGER

Most animals are in danger
Some of them are nearly extinct
Whales are being slaughtered by the second
Barn owls are losing their habitat
What is becoming of the world?
We have no right to destroy the trees
Blue whales are hunted down
We make homes, we kill animals
African elephants are in danger of death.

Michael Barton (10)
Blackmoor Park Junior School

LOVE

Love, love is pink and red,
It smells like candyfloss in a bed.

It smells, smells, smells of roses,
The family next-door have very big noses.

It feels like silk
But not like milk.

It sounds like birds singing,
But not like bells ringing.

It looks like fluffy cats,
But not like raggy mats.

All you need is love!

Olivia Ward (9)
Blackmoor Park Junior School

FOOTBALL

Roy Evans is the manager
Fowler and Owen are the strikers
Brad Freidel is new
Liverpool are the best in the world
Liverpool's home is Anfield
Which was known to Bill Shankly
He made people happy and was always
filled with glee
He was the best manager anyone could be.

Jamie McClelland (9
Blackmoor Park Junior School

FRED

I have a funny gerbil,
And his name is 'Little Fred',
Every night when I'm asleep,
He scratches in his bed,
He likes my fluffy teddy,
He loves his bed all scuffy,
He eats his food with two small paws,
And his claws he does not use.
As I said he's funny, because he eats his toys,
My gerbil is a baby boy,
Maybe I will give him some food,
When he makes too much noise I get in a mood.
My gerbil is cute,
And my gerbil plays the flute.

Lucy Smith (9)
Blackmoor Park Junior School

SCARED

It was a dark night,
The moon was full.
It was so scary,
Out alone.
All was quiet except for the sound,
Of footsteps just behind me.
I quickly turned round,
To see what it was,
But it was only a cute little dog.

Hayley Gillies (10)
Blackmoor Park Junior School

SCORING A GOAL

When you score a goal in football
The crowd calls!
And you scream with your mate
You think you've done it, great.

Your friend gives you a pat on the back
The other team's manager should get the sack.

You run along the crowd
They seem so very loud
The other team feels down and out
While we are having a great big shout.

Suddenly the whistle goes
And the ref says 'No goal!'

Hannah Stoneley (10)
Blackmoor Park Junior School

MR RABBIT

Clamp, clump as he walks through the park
As it is the same he does every day
Clamp, clump as he walks through the park
That's my pal Mr Rabbit

He has white ears
And one red nose
Brown eyes
He eats carrots
and lettuce and rabbit food.

Lauren Whittaker (9)
Blackmoor Park Junior School

COLOURS

Red is the colour of my pencil
Red is the colour of a rose
Red is the colour of my English book
Red is the colour of Rudolf's nose

Blue is the colour of my jumper
Blue is the colour of my tie
Blue is the colour of my ruler
Blue is the colour of the sky

Yellow is the colour of my maths book
Yellow is the colour of my bun
Yellow is the colour of my pencil case
Yellow is the colour of the sun.

Katie Aspinall (9)
Blackmoor Park Junior School

THE SNOW

The snow is icy, cold and wet.
I love the snow.
I love to make snowmen in the snow.
I make snowballs, I throw balls.
They are cold and wet.
I love the snow it is like ice-cream
Cold, wet and icy.
I love the snow.
I don't care what you say.
I love the snow.

Katie Taylor (9)
Blackmoor Park Junior School

THE SEA

Calm and serene at times I can be.
I glide in and out, off and on through the day.
I can carry a lot of weight.
But when I'm under pressure I can kick up a storm
and not offer safe passage to some.
I'm exposed to all life's elements, but then of course
I'm the sea.
I love the feel of the sun, it makes me feel warm and
soft to touch.
I can dance and twirl whenever I feel.
But I'm sure you can tell I'm the sea.
I have some friends who live within me.
They swim about beneath me.

Laura Carter (9)
Blackmoor Park Junior School

MY PET BULLDOG

My dog is fat and round,
And sleeps all day on the ground.
When she walks her belly flops around.
My dog Jemma sits and waits for her dinner,
And when Mum shouts 'Dinner time,'
She runs around the kitchen floor.
And when she eats her dinner,
You can hear crunch, crunch, crunch.
She plays happily every day,
When she gets her own way.

Danielle Scott (10)
Blackmoor Park Junior School

MY GOOBER LIP

I went to the dentist one day
And surely it can't be
That I want my tooth taken out.
But the dentist said
'I'm just going to check.'
When I opened my eyes
There it was my goober lip
I could not eat, for I don't know
It always felt like it was going to burst
Then one day it was gone
Yahoo! It's gone!
And good riddance
But it has not come back since.

Daniel Mealey (9)
Blackmoor Park Junior School

THE KING OF FRANCE

I once met the King of France
The jig was his favourite dance.
He sailed on the Titanic
And got into a panic
When the ship was due to sink
He soon stopped to think
About how to survive.
But a few years later
He was hit by a waiter
And now he's no longer alive.

Jennifer Gelling (10)
Blackmoor Park Junior School

THE ZOO

I'm a monkey and I'm a kangaroo
And we live in the zoo
I'm hairy but not a wimp
I am a lovely gorgeous chimp
I don't wear glasses and I'm funky
Yes you're right, I'm a monkey

I don't wear a bobble I can't give you a wish
Yes you've guessed it I'm a fish
I sometimes can live in a lake
Yes, I am, yes I'm a snake
We don't have any nails
You're right we're whales.

Rachel Sullivan (10)
Blackmoor Park Junior School

THE BACK DOOR

One cold winter's night,
I went upstairs and had a fright.
My mouth dried up
My heart beat faster than ever.
I didn't know what to do
My knees started knocking together.
I heard scary noises,
It was a loud noise.
It was a loud voice,
It said 'Kelly Kelly'
and it was my mum.

Kelly Melling (10)
Blackmoor Park Junior School

BOGEY BOY

This boy in my school
He thinks he's cool
But the thing is he's not you see
He's got 25 toes and he picks his nose
And his breath stinks like fish from the sea.

He's called Bogey Boy
He wrecks all my toys
He picks his nose and wipes it on them.

He's got no friends
And I know why
I hate him, he's vulgar and rude.

Kirsty Wilkes (10)
Blackmoor Park Junior School

BOGEY MAN

Alone in my bed with Ted
Noises coming from under the bed
Me and Ted under the blanky
We just found a dirty hanky
Deep voices, light voices, can't anyone hear the voices
I've got two choices
One to run with Ted
Two to stay in bed
What a noise it's making!
Me and Ted are shaking
Then the cat jumped up
And me and Ted woke up.

Vicky Sweeney (9)
Blackmoor Park Junior School

A POEM BASED ON THE FILM - TITANIC

Jack won his tickets
to go to America
on the Titanic.

Rose was Jack's true love.
He met her aboard the ship.
They fell in love fast.

When the ship set sail
Everybody was happy
to be on the ship.

The ship needed help!
The Titanic sent signals,
Urgent response! Please!

The Titanic sank
in the Atlantic Ocean.
It hit an iceberg.

Jack froze and then died.
Rose was very unhappy.
In the end Rose lived.

Andrea Parry, Michael Roberts, Francis Palmer,
Rebecca Leonard, Caitlin Abbott and Paul Crowley (11)
Garston RC JMI School

THE TITANIC IS LOST!

People having fun.
Sounds of laughter everywhere.
They shout at each other.

The Titanic sank.
The captain was Edward Smith.
It hit an iceberg.

The news had come in.
The crew members were frightened.
The great ship is doomed!

The musicians played
As the rushing crowd made chaos.
Music soothed some fear.

The crowd were amazed
That the Titanic had sunk.
Everyone was quiet.

Simon Hill (11)
Garston RC JMI School

GOODBYE!

Goodbye Southampton!
Farewell my hometown and friends.
Goodbye dear England!

I will see you soon.
My heart goes out to you all.
I will miss you all!

Rebecca Larsen (11)
Garston RC JMI School

THE LOSS OF THE TITANIC

In the dark, cold night
the Titanic sank because
it hit an iceberg.

It started to sink.
All the people were frightened.
Soon the lifeboats came.

Lots of people died.
Some got away in lifeboats.
Then the lights went out.

Sophie Hull (10)
Garston RC JMI School

GOODBYE

Farewell, Southampton!
Goodbye to the friends I know,
I will miss you so.

May the sea be calm.
God bless us on this sea voyage,
So farewell, England.

Elizabeth Killeen (11)
Garston RC JMI School

GOODBYE

Goodbye to my mother,
I will be back very soon.
I will miss you so.

Goodbye to my friends.
I will love you forever.
I will miss you so.

Goodbye to my love.
You are always in my thoughts.
I will miss you so.

Laura Harwood (10)
Garston RC JMI School

GOODBYE

Farewell, dear England,
Farewell to the places I know.
I do love you so.

I'll soon be married,
So farewell my carefree days.
Farewell, forever.

Sarah Nelson (10)
Garston RC JMI School

WAR

I was so scared as I hit the ground
Bombs are all around.
All of the people they must have found
Under the rubble in a great big mound.

As I think of the people who fought in the war.
They fought for us and are no more.
The most terrible things they must have saw
Before they died on the floor.

The people who died in the war,
Look at the life of one of them
As they lived
fought
and died
for us.

Jenna Holdsworth (10)
Halewood CE School

STANDING ON THE MOON

Standing on the moon
Looking around
Nothing to look at
Nothing around
All I can see are stars
Blazing brightly in the sky
Ahhhh an alien! I'm going to die
Running back to the rocket
Then it blasts-off into the sky.

Stephanie Jacobson (11)
Halewood CE School

UFO

Half the world is quiet
It's the middle of the night.
A child's looking out of a window.
He's in for a fright.
He sees something strange in the sky.
Brightly coloured lights flashing on and off.
He thought it might just fly by.
But it started getting lower and lower.
Now it was hovering just above the ground.
A blade came out of it and started chopping the grass.
The grass piled up into a mound.
Then a huge hand picked it up.
They must have been taking it back to do tests.
Then with a flash of light it sped away.
Then everything was quiet again.

Daniel McGunigle (11)
Halewood CE School

MY LITTLE MOUSE

My little mouse had big sharp teeth.
Fur on top of him and hair underneath.
Little beady eyes and a tail like a worm.
Little stumpy legs and ears like black holes.
My little mouse had a very wiggly nose.
Little flat paws and tiny little claws.
A little round mouth with whiskers at the sides.
But very sadly the little mousey died.
Now he's gone to little mousey heaven.
To live there for ever and ever.

Kim Wright (11)
Halewood CE School

TIGER

Orange and black stripes.
Sharp, pointy claws.
Soft, soft fur.
A really long tail.
Big, bright-orange eyes.
Four, big paws.
Really pointy ears.
A long, strong body.
Small, pink nose.
Sharp, jagged teeth.
A big roaring noise.
The killing machine.

The tiger!

Kirsty Roper (11)
Halewood CE School

SHARK

Sharp bloody teeth.
A pointy dorsal fin
It sticks out of the water when it closes in.
A shark's skin is rough.
A shark swims down below the water,
swimming really rough.
It locks its eyes on its prey then closes in.
Silently swimming along the bottom,
Shortens the gap between them.
It opens its mouth then *snap!*

Stuart Leadbetter (11)
Halewood CE School

MY BABY TREE

I sat and watched my baby tree
I wanted to watch it grow
I saw a little green bud sprout
And then a baby leaf
Quite a number of leaves started to spring
An amazing sight you see
Then there was a big brown trunk
And loads and loads of leaves
My tree is fully grown now
It is very, very big
It is a great big apple tree
Quick, quick come and see!

Emily Black (10)
Halewood CE School

SPACE

Space is gloomy, space is hot
like it's in a boiling pot.
Some space is cold
that no man can hold.
Space does never end
and it can't bend.
You can send a letter through space
but it will take years just to race.
What a disgrace!
In space there are aliens
ugly and green.
If you meet one
never go near it,
it could be mean!

Joseph Ryan (10)
Holy Family RC Primary School

ALIEN ON A PLANET

I'm one alien, all on my own, no one around me,
I guess you could say I'm

(isolated)

No one knows me, I'm so far away,
No friends, no nothing for me
to do every day.

I feel lonely, sad and happy in a way.
I've studied the planets and their atmosphere.
The sun burns

(it burns right through me.)

I fear the sun because it might kill me.

So far so good, I'm still alive, no one can doubt me.

(For I'm all alone.)

Kayleigh Keane (10)
Holy Family RC Primary School

COSMIC

Today I saw a spaceship that landed a mile away.
I ran and ran till I got to it, but it took me half the day,
Inside I met some aliens who said 'Come in and play,'
I said 'Okay' and they said 'Good'
and we had an
Excellent day.

Cheryl Gallagher (11)
Holy Family RC Primary School

I'M A TWINKLING STAR

I'm a twinkling star way above the clouds
no one around, no one at all.
I watch all the humans walk all day long
I wish I could be, but there's no chance at all.
One day I saw a rocket, which had humans in it
and all they said was 'Wow look, a shiny star!'
So with the corner of my eye I looked them in the face
I stared with an awful smile
and then they escaped.
I laughed at them as they screamed,
and then their rocket collapsed . . .
I didn't need to do much harm
it's just my laugh.
I'm a twinkling star, way above the clouds
I'm not really naughty
there's no chance of that,
but when I see humans I just have to laugh.

Melissa McConville (9)
Holy Family RC Primary School

COSMIC

     C rashing into spaceships, planets and all that,
        O pening the door of our shuttle and finding no
welcome mat.   S tars and moons we'll fly past on our
way to Mars.   M ake me hit you on the head
and all you'll see is stars! I will talk to aliens
in this little verse.   C razy 'O'
crazy 'O' crazy . . . crazy *universe.*

Eileen Powell (11)
Holy Family RC Primary School

36

SPACE

Space is gloomy.
Space is dark.
Space is historic.
Space is rock.
Space is adventurous.
Space is starry.
Space is terrifying.
Space is unusual.
Space is beautiful.
Space is enormous.
Why can't space be like the sky
Instead of a rocky, descending, horrible wasteland?
Why can't space be beautiful, colourful and gorgeous like
the sky?

Why?

Brendan Thompson (9)
Holy Family RC Primary School

TAKE THREE IN MY HOUSE

Naughty washing machine whispering.
Mad kettle singing.
Cold fridge humming.
Starving hoover cleaning.
Naughty hot toaster burning.
And the reason for this is because
I'm *mad!*

Michael Hepworth (9)
Holy Family RC Primary School

GREEN MARTIAN

Gooey, green, how disgusting
raving aliens run quick.
Eeee he's in disguise
extraordinary eyes
naughty, evil eyes.

Magic people look
a really good reading book.
Rabbiting people 'Shut up'
tutting is all they do.
Invigorating 'Just leave me alone'
Opposite they do whatever you say
Noisy 'Please be quiet'
Secretly they are Martians.

Craig O'Brien (9)
Holy Family RC Primary School

THE STARS

The stars are bright
shining down on you (every night.)
The stars are yellow
the moon is yellow
the sun is yellow,
everything that is yellow
is as bright as a star.

Becky Thompson (9)
Holy Family RC Primary School

MARS

I blinked.
Is Mars red?
Is Mars pink?
It's interesting to think.
But Mars is not pink.
So I look up in the sky and I wonder 'Why
Is it in the sky anyway?'
But then I realise I should have recognised
That Mars is not pink, it is red.
So instead of
Thinking that it is pink
I should not blink any more . . .
Should I?

Ashley Culvin (9)
Holy Family RC Primary School

TAKE THREE UNDER THE SEA

There is:

an angry	shark	snapping
a lovely	dolphin	dancing
a little	seahorse	bobbing
a big	whale	singing
a wobbling	jellyfish	stinging

And now I'm swimming to shore!

Gemma Scattergood (9)
Holy Family RC Primary School

SPACE

Space is bright coming right behind you.
Space is dark, spooky and noisy.
Space is hot in a boiling pot.
Space is cold that no man can hold.
In space you see Martians.
They rip you, tear you and eat you.
Space is a never ending place and it can't bend.
Space is a sparkling place and it's a rocky,
Groovy place that no one has been before.
Space is bright and colourful and hairy.
Space is dark and gloomy and scary.
Space is black, brown and wary.
Space is shiny, limey and starry.

Sean Kennerley (9)
Holy Family RC Primary School

TAKE THREE

In my history book there is:

A mad mummy screaming
A rotten Roman raiding
A vicious Viking sailing
A grumpy Greek mumbling
A dopey dino dancing
And I'm becoming a mad magician.

Daniel Fox (8)
Holy Family RC Primary School

COLOURS

Space is black,
Feelings are green,
So many things
I have not seen.
Bones are white,
Blood is red,
A yellow brain
Inside your head.
Muscles are red,
Wind is blue,
So many things I cannot see,
Can you?

Ceara Watson (7)
Holy Family RC Primary School

TAKE THREE IN MY COUNTRY

There is:

A bright sun shining
A deafening thunder crashing
A wet rain splashing
An electric lightning frightening
An icy snow floating

And now I'm running in!

Jennifer Reay (8)
Holy Family RC Primary School

I HEARD A BANG IN SPACE

It was noisy all day
I fell asleep on my bed.
I was dreaming about something weird in my head.
There was a big bang on Earth
On top of the planet.
This is how it began
Bang! Bang! Bang!
Beautiful! Brilliant! Boss! *Bang!*
Bright! Bouncing! Banging! Bang!

Bang! Bang!
Bang!

Emma Jones (10)
Holy Family RC Primary School

MY SISTER JAMIE

My sister Jamie is the colour lime-green.
She is a cute little hamster.
My sister Jamie is a hot sunny day.
She is a small mini-skirt.
Jamie is a soft, comfy armchair.
She is the programme 'Friends'.
My sister Jamie is fish and chips with gravy.
Jamie is the best sister anybody could ever have.

Hayley Clarke
Holy Family RC Primary School

SPACE

Space is bright as bright as the sun!
I wonder what it will be like . . .
It might be fun
Would you go up in space?
It's probably a nice old place!
I wonder what it's like up there?
I don't know who really cares
Everybody talks about that place.
I think space is a funny old place.

Joanne Parry (10)
Holy Family RC Primary School

SUN

The sun is hot for there you know,
For all the hotness seems to grow.
It grows and grows until it stops
And then it all seems to drop!
It drops to make you very brown.
It drops to make you cool and sound.
Then the browness goes away
And I think I'm fading away.

Therese Melvin (10)
Holy Family RC Primary School

TAKE THREE AT THE ZOO

At the zoo there are:

Hungry lions roaring
Fat elephants bathing
Baby penguins swimming
Stripy tigers jumping
Spotty cheetahs running

And they're all driving me mad!

Anna Kyle (9)
Holy Family RC Primary School

YOUR DOG, MY DOG

My dog is black,
Your dog is white.
My dog stayed at home,
Your dog had a fight.

My dog is smart,
Your dog is not.
My dog sat around,
Your dog played a lot.

My dog supports Everton,
Your dog supports Liverpool.
My dog acted dumb,
Your dog acted cool.

Our dogs have nothing in common,
As you can see.
But we have,
You and me.

Rebecca Goldstein (11)
Holy Name JMI School

KIDS

Clever kids,
Homework kids,
Bunking-off school kids.
Maths kids,
Science kids,
Name on the board kids.

Kids, kids, kids.

Football kids,
Dancing kids,
Tap, ballet, disco kids.
Netball kids,
Swimming kids,
Jumping up and down kids.

Kids, kids, kids.

Naughty kids,
Sporty kids,
Dotty kids,
Spotty kids,
Ugly kids,
Pretty kids.

Kids, kids, kids.

Scary kids,
Hairy kids,
Messy kids,
Dressy kids,
Scruffy kids,
Mouth full of chocolate kids.

Kids, kids, kids,

Stephanie Kewley (11)
Holy Name JMI School

MAN FAT

Man fat
Top hat
Fell flat
Squashed hat
Made flat
Smelt bad
Died flat.

Simba Muzavazi (10)
Holy Name JMI School

I HEAR

When I wake up in the morning
I hear people talking
I hear dogs barking
I hear cats purring
I hear the wind whistling
I hear everything.

Alex Gough (10)
Holy Name JMI School

MOTHER'S DAY

Mother's Day is three weeks away,
Lovely presents, chocolates, flowers.
I'll put my feet up for a few hours.
Wash, clean, cook and iron,
even though it's Mother's Day
the time is not mine.

Natalie McCormick (10)
Holy Name JMI School

MY DOG BESS

My dog Bess
Makes a terrible mess.
She hangs from the washin'
And makes it rotten.
She chewed Mum's money
I thought it was funny.
She's soft as a bunny
She rolls on her back
And makes me laugh.
She barks, *Yap! Yap!*
And I go *Clap! Clap!*
She goes for a run
To have some fun.
I throw the ball
And she plays football.
And that's my dog Bess!
Yes! Yes!

David Gallagher (11)
Holy Name JMI School

FLY

Fly on the window,
Fly on the door,
Fly in the living room,
Fly on the floor.
Mum gets the spray out,
holds on tight,
Seems like Mum's
just won the fight.

Jenni Callaghan (10)
Holy Name JMI School

LADY

I have a little doggy
Lady is her name
And when I take her off the lead
She won't come back again.

This really is a problem
As I hope you will agree
As Lady will not listen
When I call her back to me.

It really is a headache
Every time I take her out
So could anybody help me
'Cause I really am in doubt.

Carla English (10)
Holy Name JMI School

LIVERPOOL, MY TEAM

Liverpool is my favourite team.
When they play I jump and scream.
When they lose I get the blues.
When they win I get a grin.
The game has begun and the ball has been spun,
Fowler has run as fast as he can,
To get the ball so that Owen can score,
And get the crowd to jump and roar.
I'm glad this game is not a bore.

Thomas Roberts (10)
Holy Name JMI School

I WONDER!

I wonder why I'm lying here.
I wonder why I'm sitting here.
I wonder why I'm me.

I wonder why I have a name.
I wonder why I see.
I wonder why I smell.

I wonder why I'm getting up.
I wonder why I'm walking.
I wonder if we'll do some
more wondering tomorrow.

I wonder!

Alex Ashton (11)
Holy Name JMI School

MY SPELL

Rats, bats, cats,
Smelly frogs,
Horrible hogs.

Put them in a cauldron
Stir them, stir them,
Round and round,
Until you have found.

My horrible spell!

Catherine Jones (10)
Holy Name JMI School

JIMMY

My dog Jimmy is very skinny,
Despite the fact that he eats the local cats.
Jimmy, Jimmy, Jimmy.

Jimmy is hairy but not that scary,
His long, black hair only scares a teddy bear.
Jimmy, Jimmy, Jimmy.

Jimmy has the longest legs,
And the fluffiest tail.
He likes to bite the milkman,
And the man who brings the mail.
Jimmy, Jimmy, Jimmy.

Francis Fearon (11)
Holy Name JMI School

SPRING

An early spring morning,
Sunlight comes through the curtains,
Then for a moment,
I stopped to listen
To birds whistling along with the wind.
It was a lovely song.
Dogs were barking for an early morning walk.
I see the sun shining,
Flowers beginning to grow,
Soon the gardeners will be here to mow.

Natalie Hill (10)
Holy Name JMI School

SMILES!

The other day I read a poem and thought I'd have a go.
It was about smiling in the sunshine, rain, hail, or the snow.
I guess you think that it's silly to smile upon the rain, hail, or snow.
But other people will see you smiling and might just have a go.
Then they will be following in your footsteps and people will follow
in theirs,
The earth will be a better place with smiling through the air.
I guess there's a moral to this poem that's been passed from smile
to smile,
I think I know the moral -

'Every cloud has a silver lining'!

Natalie Palmer (11)
Holy Name JMI School

MISS HUMBLE

The old witch, Miss Humble,
Used to always fly on her little brown broomstick up in the sky.

But now Miss Humble doesn't like it anymore,
Because her powers are fading and she will drop to the floor.

So now Miss Humble is upset and sad,
Because she is always crying and she feels really bad.

Miss Humble is now happy,
And no more attempts to fly,
On her little brown broomstick up in the sky.

Megan Fergus (9)
Holy Name JMI School

ROSE

There once was a girl called Rose,
Who had enormous toes
She had the worst habit
Just like a little rabbit,
She picked and picked her toes.
She picks them in class and picks them at home
She just picks and picks and picks her toes.
Her mum and dad said, 'Rose you're bad,'
They were so ashamed, they felt so sad.
Her toe began to grow so small,
But still she picked more and more.
She cried, 'Why me?'
She was a sight to see.
One crutch in the left hand
A bandage on her right hand
And a bandage on her foot.
But still she did not stop.
Her mother said, 'Oh Rose you are dumb,
to pick your toes, and not suck your thumb.'
Then one day when she woke up
Her hand went down to her foot
And by amazement no toe was there
Not even a nail or a piece of dirt.
So don't *you* be like disgusting Rose.

Jenna Burden (11)
Mackets CP School

I HAVE SEEN THE WIND

I have seen the wind blowing in my street,
It always sweeps people right off their feet.

I have seen the wind blowing in the trees,
Splitting them in half and making people sneeze.

I have seen the wind blowing all the sea,
Knocking on the boat, I'm glad it wasn't me.

I have seen the wind blowing all the smoke,
And making us choke.

Thomas McNiven (8)
Mackets CP School

DOLPHINS

They glide through the water
With graceful expertise
A wondrous sight to see a dolphin
Upon our deep blue seas

Always smiling or so it seems
Happy to swim and play
I wish I could be a dolphin
If only for a day

So why are they in danger
From man, who's supposed to be
The most intelligent life-form
On land or in the sea.

Why can't man realise
This earth is made for all to share
Not just for them to kill and hunt
For meat and skin and fur.

The dolphin is my favourite
But all have the right to peace
So let's start living together
And let the killing cease.

Diane Reeves (11)
Mackets CP School

I HAVE SEEN THE WIND

I have seen the wind
Whistling through the trees
Over my head
And down at my knees.

I have seen the wind
Untidying the street
It makes me trip over
My own two feet.

I have seen the wind
Roaring through the keyhole
The fire is dying
It needs more coal.

I have seen the wind
Pushing clouds through the sky
They're saying goodbye
With a big sigh.

Shelly Duggan (8)
Mackets CP School

I HAVE SEEN THE WIND

I have seen the wind
Blowing in my street
It's not my fault
That it blows me off my feet.

I have seen the wind
Make the trees sway from side to side
The branch fell in my garden
And my cat nearly died.

I have seen the wind
Making the waves go higher
And the lifeguards have to rescue
A ship that's on fire.

I have seen the wind
Blow the clouds away
And there is a loud noise
When the children come out to play.

Kate Holly Brown (9)
Mackets CP School

I HAVE SEEN THE WIND

I have seen the wind
Blowing down my street
Pulling civilians
Right off their feet.

My mum came back
From the windy street
She looked weird from her head
Right down to her feet.

I see the tornado wind
Blowing trees down
The very next day
It's a gentle breeze.

In our street
There's a gentle breeze
But not
In the howling seas.

Philip David Jameson (8)
Mackets CP School

GLISTENING SKY

Stars glitter in the sky
They never go away,
   They stay in the sky all day
They never go away.
   One day they will explode
And fly away.
   And in your mind you will have
                              a picture
Of their glistening face.

Kate Sutton (10)
Mackets CP School

THE WIND

I have seen the wind, blowing in my street
I have seen the wind, blowing me off my feet.
I have seen tornadoes whizzing around
It makes me feel dizzy
As I spin around on the ground.

Marc Robinson (8)
Mackets CP School

DIANA

Diana the Princess of Wales,
Diana the Queen of Hearts,
Diana was kind and caring,
Diana you were the loving one.

Robert Segar (9)
Mackets CP School

ALL ABOUT ME

John is my name
Football is my game
Man United I hate
Liverpool FC are just great.
My favourite player is Michael Owen
And this is my poem.

John Coffey 10)
Mackets CP School

SPRINGTIME

S pring is here.
P eople enjoy the warm weather.
R unning through fields playing games.
I   n the lovely warm sun.
N ice gentle baby lambs are born.
G reat times we have in spring.

Kayleigh Large (10)
Mackets CP School

ZOOMING ZOO

Squiggles squeaking
Hippos hopping
Zebras zooming
Elephants eating
Racing reptiles
Leaping lions.

Melissa Ryan (8)
Mackets CP School

MY SISTERS

I hate my little sister
She moans and groans and screams
But then again my big sister can be very mean.
Why can't I have a brother,
To rough and tumble and fight.
The only time it's quiet
Is when the girls are asleep at night.

Christian Ryan (10)
Mackets CP School

CHRISTMAS

Great Britain - Christmas Eve

Tonight the silver moon shivers
White frost glitters on hills
Children sing round a Christmas tree
that glints in its tinsel frills.
They munch on mince pies.

Stephanie Calveley (7)
Mackets CP School

SUMMER

S   is for the summer's sun.
U   is for us rolling down the hill.
M   is for messing in the muddy field.
M   is for lambs playing in the meadows.
E   is for Easter.
R   is for a bouncing rabbit.

Philip Soo (10)
Mackets CP School

TIME FOR SCHOOL

It's time for school
It's where you're cool,
You meet your mates,
At the school gates.

You line-up like a nervous wreck,
To go in and sit at your desk,
I fell over in school today,
Then I went out to play.

The first person to go in for dinner,
Shouts out 'I'm the winner,'
Some of the dinners are so, so nice,
And the milk is as cold as ice.

Sarah Jane Cartwright (10)
Mackets CP School

I HAVE SEEN THE WIND

I have seen the wind
Blowing the leaves off the trees,
Trees falling down the street
Sticks falling like they have no feet.
Grass blowing from side to side
While the rest fades away today.
Trees blowing from side to side
Wishing they could fly,
You never know they might blow
Into the sky so high.

Scott Holt (9)
Mackets CP School

MOTHER'S DAY

It was a lovely Sunday morning
The sun was nice and bright
And I felt a little tired
'Cos I'd gone to bed quite late.

Then I just remembered
that it was Mother's Day
And I woke my mum up shouting
Guess what day it is today?

So I gave her a hug and kiss
And made her toast and tea
And I gave her a Mother's Day card
Made specially by me.

David Pownall (9)
Mackets CP School

THE QUEEN

There once as a queen
Who wasn't very clean,
So she hired a maid,
Who wasn't well-paid.
The maid went searching with her broom,
Cleaning from room to room.
By the end of the day she was filled with dismay,
When she had finally seen,
That the queen was so mean
and unclean.

Jenny Johnson (9)
Mackets CP School

HARVEY

He scurries round his cage at night
  As happy as can be
He's the cutest thing around
  And he belongs to me.

His fur is soft, so golden brown,
  In parts so snowy white
He prefers to sleep all day
  He's a creature of the night.

I love him more than words can say
  He's the best in the world that's true
It's Harvey my little hamster
  And he loves me too!

Katie Baker (10)
Mackets CP School

DIANA

Diana you are the caring one,
Diana you are the
woman who helps all
those who suffer,
Diana you are the best,
better than all the rest.
Diana when it is night
the stars spell out your name.
Diana you will always be
my shining star.

Philip Cliff (8)
Mackets CP School

I HAVE SEEN THE WIND

I have seen the wind
blowing in my street.
Blowing down my trousers
and tickling my little feet.

As the wind blows the clouds
over your little head.
I am glad that my little head
was tucked up in bed.

I have seen the wind
blowing a balloon away.
I wonder where it will end up?
Someone may find it some day.

Michael Soo (8)
Mackets CP School

10 THINGS TO DO

Number one,   I eat my scone
Number two,   I make hot stew
Number three, I have a cup of tea
Number four,   there's someone at the door
Number five,   I talk to Clive
Number six,   I eat a Twix
Number seven, I'm going to Devon
Number eight, I'm fixing the gate.
Number nine, I hang the washing on the line
Number ten,   time to start all over again.

Leanne Gault (11)
Mackets CP School

I HAVE SEEN THE WIND

I have seen the wind
Blowing in the trees
So when the wind starts
It gives me a sneeze.

I have seen the wind
Blowing the seas
Making such big waves
Even in a gentle breeze.

I have seen the wind
Blowing the smoke from the fire
As the flames rise
Growing higher and higher.

Rachael Quayle (8)
Mackets CP School

A LIST OF MY DREAMS

A teddy, a pen,
A lovely soap set
Teletubby teddies
A cyberpet.

A pad of paper,
A dog with a lead
A little brown kitten
For me to feed.

I would like a computer
A laptop would be nice
A PC would be better
Than a board game and dice.

Natalie McDonald (10)
Mackets CP School

ANIMALS

The fierce ones are the tiger and cheetah,
While the tame ones star on Blue Peter.
Blue whales and dolphins are both mammals,
But the amazing ones I think, are the camels.

Cats and dogs are good for pets,
But they have to go to all different vets.
Sharks and fish swim down in the sea,
While this one flies high, yes it's a bee!

Monkeys mostly eat bananas,
But pigs and cows make mess for farmers.
African elephants have very big ears,
But endangered animals sometimes have tears.

Stevi Chapman (10)
Mackets CP School

I HAVE SEEN THE WIND

I have seen the wind
Blowing in my street
I have no idea
Why it doesn't have any feet.

I have seen the wind
Blowing in the park
But I am going home
Because it is getting dark.

I have seen the wind
Blowing the smoke
And when the fog comes
I really choke.

Mark Wheatley (9)
Mackets CP School

I HAVE SEEN THE WIND

I have seen the wind
Blowing people about
Sometimes I can't
Even hear them shout.

I have seen the wind,
Blowing up the street
I think it's going
After my feet.

I have seen the wind
Blowing out to sea
Ships trying to sail against the gale
I'm glad it's not me!

Hayley Walker (8)
Mackets CP School

WINTER

Ring, ring, ringing of the alarm bell,
Get up, get up, it's winter.
Running downstairs chattering my teeth,
As I grab my coat and stamp my feet.
I run outside and get in the car.
'Oh no!' my mum says, 'It will not start.'
As she turns the key the car just says,
'I'm too cold to go!'
As we get out of the car we hear our feet
Slushing in the snow.
As the next door neighbour says, 'Hello.'
On a cold winter's day.

Gemma Murphy (10)
Norman Pannell School

WINTER DAYS

The sky is grey today
The icicles are crashing to the ground .
Gales are chilly
Thick fog all around.
Frozen roadside
Crisp snow falling
Gracefully to the ground.
Lightning flashing,
Thunder roaring.
Refreshing rain
Some people say,
And that's only in one day!

Caroline Hampson (10)
Norman Pannell School

MY BEST FRIEND

Emma is my best friend
Our friendship will never end
Emma shares
Emma cares
Emma will always stick by my side
She will never run and hide
Emma is my best friend
Our friendship will never end.

Allyce Midghall (10)
Norman Pannell School

THE TOUCH OF FROST

Winter is a cold day,
Staying in bed all night and day
Playing out with freezing hands
And shiny noses too.
Children playing snowball fights
On this frosty winter night
Feeling ice makes me feel like a warm bed
Hearing bells go ring, ring
Different coloured hats and scarves
Winter is a cold time.

Helen McKenna (10)
Norman Pannell School

HARVEST

Falling leaves all the time,
I pick them up, they now are mine.
We go to the market to buy some fish,
They're every colour you could wish.
Ears of wheat upon the floor,
I think I would like some more.
Juicy pears, golden wheat,
Thank you harvest for the food we eat.

Kate Stulberg (10)
Norman Pannell School

FIREWORKS

Whooshing, whizzing,
Sparklers sizzling.
Crackling, whistling,
Fireworks sizzling.
Banging, booming,
Rockets zooming.
Fountains gleaming,
Roman candles beaming.
Teeth chattering,
Adults nattering.

Karl Rawlinson (10)
Norman Pannell School

WINTER IS

Winter is cold
This is what winter holds.
Christmas, Boxing Day, New Year too
All of these occasions are all for you
Winter is a time to stay in your bed
Just pull over your covers and tuck in your head
And mountains of snow
But the car won't go!

Kelly Corrin (10)
Norman Pannell School

WHEN I THINK OF WINTER

When I think of winter I think of biting air,
I think of wise men who brought gifts of gold, frankincense
and myrrh,
I also think of all the street buried under snow,
And sometimes I think of when the car won't go.
When I think of winter it's hard not to forget . . .
That on Christmas morn outside, it's usually sloppy and wet.
When I think of winter I think of getting a red nose,
And instead of getting up early I have a longer doze.

Kayleigh Griffith (10)
Norman Pannell School

HARVEST

Shiny conkers,
Bright yellow corn,
Throughout the year harvest's store.
Silver fish,
A tasty dish,
All the food from the sea that we could wish.
Juicy fruits,
Grains of wheat,
Thank you harvest for the foods we eat.

Clare Lawrence (10)
Norman Pannell School

A FIREWORKS' DISPLAY

Loud fireworks up in the air
Bang, whizzing everywhere.
Children laughing,
Adults yapping.
People shout hooray
What a wonderful display!
Fireworks whizzing,
Some are fizzing.
It's a nice night of sounds.

Debbie Sanderson (10)
Norman Pannell School

WATCH TV

When I get in
Have a drink
Dinner
Sit down
By myself
Watch TV
Wild House
The Demon Headmaster.

Go to my nan's
Watch more TV
Cartoon Network

Put my 'jamas on
Sleep
Dream about TV.

Mark Molyneaux (14)
Palmerston School

FOOTBALL

Tonight I'm going to watch football
Liverpool and Celtic are on
We've got tickets me and Roy
Just me and Roy

We just get there
We go and look at the trophies
Take a photograph
Go and sit down

8 o'clock kick-off
And the football starts
Lots of people there
The ambulance man comes
Somebody's hurt a leg

Liverpool scores, the ball's in the goal
The wave says:
'Liverpool, Liverpool, Liverpool'.

Michael Price (14)
Palmerston School

PEACE

Peace is like a dove that gives light and care
Peace is the light of the world,
Peace is caring and sharing.
You can be a peacemaker if you believe in peace.
You can be a peacemaker by stopping fights,
Getting on with your work,
Helping people with their problems.
Please make peace in the world.

Leanne Byrne (11)
St Andrew's RC Primary School

PEACE POEM

Where there is despair in wars and fighting,
Let hope's halo shine.
Where there is injury and murder,
Let hope's halo shine.

When dark reigns the world,
Let light awake from sleep.
When dark shadows the world,
Let light awake from sleep.

When arguing splits us apart,
Reunion is at hand.
When arguing takes over us,
Reunion is at hand.

Bullying is mean and all this calling names,
But friendship is the best.
Bullying gets thumbs down
Friendship is the best.

Bombs verses scanners, the match is uneven.
Peace shines through and has the victory.

Lauren Hansen (9)
St Andrew's RC Primary School

MY PEACE POEM

If you're sometimes being bad,
If you've made somebody sad.
Take your peace and share
Show that person that you care.

If you're sometimes being mean,
Don't make mess for Mum to clean.
Have a heart, share your love,
Follow in the path of a dove.

If you've got a sister or brother,
Get along with one another.
Don't fight, carry a smile,
Make your friendship worthwhile.

If you're most times sharing sweets,
If you're most times making peace.
You're showing people that you care,
By all that peace you share.

Damon Daniels (11)
St Andrew's RC Primary School

PEACE POEM

Bombs going off making the ground ruffle
Gun shots going off in the peaceful countryside
People talking, listening to each other
Peace descends like the wings on a dove.

Angry arguing at home, at school and at play
Hatred spills out shouting and screaming
Punching and hitting turning into devils
Violence in the streets, gunshots going off
People shouting 'Help.'

But all is well, peaceful people trying to live their little lives
While bombs go off making their lives a misery
But they just take it all in
Their families live peaceful lives with happiness and joy
They say it's like angels walking you to Heaven's gate.

They all live a different life now in another little town
In that town there is peace everywhere they walk
They say their friendship there is very happy
No bombs going off just peace in that town.

Laura Atkinson (10)
St Andrew's RC Primary School

PEACE POEM

Peace is like children laughing in hot sunlight.
Hatred can come in the way of peace.
When I am in a room of darkness only the light of peace can
                                        bring a light.
When thunder is looming on the window there is anger.
When gentle snowflakes come down there is peace.
When there is war and fighting there is no peace.
When there is wickedness peace will protect you.
Peace is like a chorus of angels.
Peace is like a brightly shining star.
Peace is like a candle of friendship
A person who is selfish or not caring is not a peacemaker.
Hopes and dreams of peace, *let them come true.*
The drums play before the war of peace.
Red is the colour of anger, white is the colour of peace.
People are being bullied let's bring peace.
Everybody has a special part of them that has peace, let's show it.
The magic dove holds the power of peace, let's find out.
Let us show our peace.

Natalie Goulding (9)
St Andrew's RC Primary School

PEACE

Peace is joy and love
The sign of peace is the dove

If you are a peacemaker
Keep the peace and don't break it

If there is a fight and you break it up
Never forget to never give up

When your heart is filled with joy
Remember peace is not a toy

A hug is also peace
If you keep it on it will increase

Peace can also be made if we work together
If we work hard enough peace can last forever.

Hayley Potter (11)
St Andrew's RC Primary School

THE WORLD IS DARKNESS

The world is darkness,
We are the Light.

The world is dying,
Let us bring life.

The world is hurt,
Let us cure it.

The world will make peace,
We will help.

The world is curing,
Let us give thanks.

The world will help all,
We will keep praying.

The world will guide us,
Let us follow close.
The world is light.

David Barton-Cowley (10)
St Andrew's RC Primary School

PEACE POEM

'Help' I hear from the crying war child
'Save me!' from the distressed mothers
'No!' yell the victims
'*Bang*!, shouts the evil bomb
Where is the peace in this land?

Smiles of joy are peaceful
Warm sunsets of orange and red keep our peace
Angels bounce on fluffy clouds
'Shalom my friend' says the wise man
Doves fly in the wilderness.

'Give me your lunch money!' threatens the bully.
Tears of sadness stream down the poor child's face.
'Help me please, does anyone care?' they say in their dreams.
Use some of your peace here Lord.

Sweet music fills your ears
Lord God please spread all of your peace around the world.

Hayley Rignall (10)
St Andrew's RC Primary School

PEACE PRAYER

P eace is like a dove flying through the sky
E verybody has love and peace inside them
A nd the people who are peacemakers are kind and loving
C aring people are nice and kind
E verybody who is not a peacemaker try to be a peacemaker.

Alex Walpole (10)
St Andrew's RC Primary School

PEACE THAT YOU CAN SHARE

Be kind to your family and friends
Share peace that never ends
Peace will remind you of a dove
And show your family that you love them

If you are being selfish
Don't be naughty
Remember that people are nice to you
            if you are nice to them
Follow in the steps of a dove

If you're being horrible to your brother or sister
Don't just share your peace
Don't be cheeky
Be kind and share your peace with everyone
And if you remember to be kind and share your peace,
Others will be kind and share their peace
            with you and everyone.

Andrea Jackson (11)
St Andrew's RC Primary School

PEACE POEM

P eace is something that we should use every day
E verlasting harmony
A nd all the caring, sharing and loving
C aring for others is good
E njoy a world of peace
F ill this world with harmony
U ninteresting people leave others to be the peacemaker
L et everyone be a peacemaker.

Andrew Smith (10)
St Andrew's RC Primary School

PEACE WILL MAKE YOU SMILE

Peace will make you happy,
Mile after mile it would make people smile,
The world could be as peaceful as a dove,
Everywhere there could be love,
Don't leave someone alone to cry
You can make people happy if you try.

Share your love and friendliness,
So the world can escape this war filled mess,
If people give a little time,
All lives would be better yours and mine,
If everyone helped each other
We would all be united like sister and brother.

If you try to be kind,
There is something you will find
Your heart will be filled with joy
If you help every girl and boy.

Helen Jacobsen (11)
St Andrew's RC Primary School

PEACE POEM

P eace is like a group of angels singing sweetly
E rupting volcanoes are like a great big war in the night
A lways spread peace like a big kite flying in the air
C urses spreading around the world
E verlasting peace (as always) loving and kind people cry.

P ollution everywhere killing everyone
O n the world there is a great big heart full of love
E xploding bombs are like a loud lion roaring
M any loving people are filled with peace.

Victoria Scahill (10)
St Andrew's RC Primary School

PEACE

You can make peace
at home and in school,
maybe do all the dishes.

Be good and obey the rules,
talk to someone who is lonely.
Cheer up a friend,
give Mum a treat,
give her breakfast in bed,
help Granddad in the garden.
Don't fight, and say *no*.

Spread peace all around you,
to all that you know.
Help others to be good
just like
they should.

Paul George (10)
St Andrew's RC Primary School

PEACE POEM

P is for perfect days a sunny and beautiful time.
E is for exploding bombs blowing up houses everywhere.
A is for a glowing angel with sparkling golden hair.
C is for crying children in the remains of a war that killed their parents.
E is for everywhere quiet, calm and peaceful.

P is for peace, a dove of holy friendship.
O is for outbursts of disaster ruining people's lives.
E is for everywhere safe *no* wars.
M is for mourning for everyone who has died.

Elizabeth Cousins (10)
St Andrew's RC Primary School

PEACE POEM

Peace means love and friendship,
Not hate and fear,
Peace means joy and happiness,
Not killing and death,
Let's not fight,
Let's all be friends,
Let's shake hands,
Let's make amends,
Appreciate each other,
No matter what colour skin we have,
Save our world which we take advantage of,
And ruin with our hate,
Let's be friends,
It does not matter what religion we are.

Tami Harper (11)
St Andrew's RC Primary School

MY PEACE POEM

I try to make peace wherever I am,
I try to make peace with people I know,
Everywhere I go I will make peace
With everyone I meet I will make peace.
Where there is no love let me bring peace
Where there is war let me bring peace
With no peace it would be like the world had come to an end.
Without peace we would have no friend.

Chantelle Kerrigan (10)
St Andrew's RC Primary School

MAKING PEACE

We can make peace by doing so many things,
When we make peace we are free of sins
Peace is a sign of happiness and love.
The most special sign of peace is the peace dove
Peace can be made with brothers and sisters or a mum or dad.
To me peace can never be bad
True peace lasts forever,
Peace can be made if we work together
The world would be a better place,
If we all put on a smiling face
And if we all stay close and near.
We will be happy each and every year
So if everybody everywhere said a little prayer and started to care,
I think life would be fair.

Helen Range (10)
St Andrew's RC Primary School

MY PEACE POEM

Our world is falling apart
Our world is covered with hate
Our world is filled with war
Our world is weaker than ever
But it might not be too late.
So if we work together and be like a dove
We can make this world we live in filled
With lots of love.

John Moore (10)
St Andrew's RC Primary School

PEACE

Let me be a peacemaker,
and let me bring peace.
Where there is sadness,
let me bring happiness.
Peace comes from the dove of peace,
and it spreads it across the world,
everyone should be peaceful.
Everyone should share,
but most of all,
we should make peace with our friends.
The dove of peace
brings it to everybody.
Share your love,
with everyone.

Suzanne Prescott (11)
St Andrew's RC Primary School

PEACE

Peace and love is everywhere
Hugs and kisses are in the air
War can break out but always smile
For peace can be around all of the while
Do not fight do not be silly
Be good and kind but don't act pretty
Just be normal just be you
You're kind enough so I like you
But if you're bad and not very kind
Peace will come along and change your mind!

Joanne Griffiths (11)
St Andrew's RC Primary School

PEACE POEM

War is like a raging earthquake destroying all in its path
Bang, bang, bang guns banging everywhere
Lightning and thunder destroying the sky
Talking listening understanding brings peace

Peace is like a happy cheerful smile
Sunsets, rainbows shining in the sky
Peace is like a dream come true

Peace is like a cool gentle waterfall

Fighting is like lightning and thunder arguing in the sky
People arguing, calling names at each other
Kicking, punching, hitting
Peace is very nice.

Lorna Duffy (10)
St Andrew's RC Primary School

PEACE IS LOVE

Lord where there is war
   let me bring peace to the world.
Peace is like a dove in the sky
   be nice to people.
Love can come at home, in school
   or on the playground.
Everybody has peace inside them
   try to be good and loving.
Don't hit and kick
   if you're bad be a peacemaker
I like peace because it is love.

Daniel O'Neill (11)
St Andrew's RC Primary School

PEACE

Hatred is like a field of thorns and thistles waiting for someone to grab.
Love is like a mother holding a newborn baby in her arms tightly.
Wars are like explosions of bombs destroying the world.
Kindness is like a best friend comforting you when you're sad.

Selfishness is when someone won't give you something
                                          because you're different.
Hope is like a comforting family wishing you the best in life.
Despair is like a part of you is gone.
Sleep is like a dreamy heaven with an angel comforting you
                                          with all your favourite things.

Bombs are like an exploding volcano killing all things in its way.
Angels at night make you secure and tight.

Sara Mahamy (9)
St Andrew's RC Primary School

THE DOVE

Let me bring peace to the world,
Peace is so great, the whole world should share it.
But where people don't share peace, let me share it.
The world is covered in hate,
Hate can be overcome by peace.
Peace is a large white dove,
It should have widespread wings that cover the earth,
But some people deny peace.
Where this happens let me be the dove,
With widespread white wings.
Peace and harmony should fall from the dove's wings,
And cover the world with peace.

Matthew Cawley (11)
St Andrew's RC Primary School

PEACE

Peace is like a dove, peace means love.
Share and be kind, be happy and joyful.
Don't be sad and dull,
Be happy and helpful!

Lord let peace be in everyone's heart,
Lord let peace be everywhere.
Let peace stop every war, every fight and every quarrel.

Help everyone to live in peace,
Help everyone to be peaceful
So sometimes if you're bad
Show everyone you can share, show everyone care and show help!

Sarah Martin (10)
St Andrew's RC Primary School

DARKNESS

I hate the darkness.
So scary, so eerie,
So silent, so deadly.
So full of awful things
Like monsters and witches and bats and snakes.
Dead men's fingers reach out like rakes,
Pulling me out of my safe, warm bed.
The ghosts of the darkness won't stop till I'm dead!
I really hate the darkness.
So scary,
So eerie,
So silent,
So deadly,
So full of awful things!

Kaylea Allport (11)
St Cuthbert's JMI School

Nothing To Do

Nothing to do, nothing to do,
Put some Army ants right down the loo.
Bang a pickaxe through the stairs,
When Dad comes in pull out his hairs.

Go to the fruit shop buy a grape,
Travel to the zoo make the keeper go ape.
Annoy your brother whack his face,
Or go to the museum, (to steal a mace).

Drive your mum round the bend,
Someone asks you for money, say, 'I've got none to lend.'
Get a knife, make sure it's jagged,
Then cut up clothes, only ones that are ragged.

Make an electric circuit and overheat your wire,
Now enter a church, throw tomatoes at the choir.
Draw a picture and draw it bad,
Remember a sad memory of a pet that you had.

Listen to some music, some music with a beat,
Stand by a fire, *cor blimey!* You can feel the heat.
Go to a farm, a farm which has some sheep,
Or if you're still bored then *go to sleep.*

Joel Canavan (10)
St Cuthbert's JMI School

My Rabbit

My rabbit eats like a horse,
It eats lettuce and carrots of course.
It eats every day in the month of May,
And gets fatter and fatter of course.

My rabbit was small and meek at first,
But now she looks like she's going to burst.
But nevertheless we think she's the best,
And we will keep her every day until she dies.

Nina Orr (10)
St Cuthbert's JMI School

PITCH BLACK

I climb into my bed, I look around,
I see shadows.
I hear a noise.
Could it be a witch on a big broomstick
with her black cat?
No it's just my brother in his room.
I close my eyes, I try to go to sleep,
but no I cannot.
I sit up, I look around.
I want to put the light on but I cannot.
I wish I could go to sleep.
I hear my brother snoring,
I hear a crashing sound.
It is like an elephant coming down the steps.
But no it is just my mum in the kitchen.
Oh no I cannot go to sleep.
Then it is silent.
I think my mum and dad are coming to bed.
My mum comes in and says,
'Are you still awake? Go to sleep now.'
Then my eyes get weak and I go to sleep.

Anjalee Carney (10)
St Cuthbert's JMI School

ALL IN A DAY

In the morning,
I am always yawning.
I'm not going down those creaky stairs
or sitting on those squeaky chairs.
'Get down these stairs,' my mum said.
'I'm not bringing you breakfast in bed
put on your summer dress
and please don't make a scruffy mess.'
Finally I found a way down those creaky stairs.
Oh no please don't make me sit on those squeaky chairs!
Get in the brand new car.
'Mummy I want a chocolate bar.'
'No, you're going to school.
I've just got to stop to get some fuel.'
'Mum we're going to be late,
then no one will be my mate.'
We're going home from school now,
'Mummy can I play with my toys.'
'No they make too much noise.
I'm making your tea.'
'Mum, Dillan's flicking a pea.'
'Go and watch telly
and you can have some jelly.'
It's bedtime now.
'Get upstairs
and say your prayers.'
Good night!

Jenny Morris (10)
St Cuthbert's JMI School

88

WIGGLES AND GIGGLES

I have the giggles
I have the wiggles
I giggle and wiggle
I wiggle and giggle
If I wiggle once more
I'll crack the floor
If I giggle once more
I'll fall off my chair
If I don't stop
I'll be in trouble
If I don't stop
I'll split into double
Giggle, giggle, wiggle
Wiggle, wiggle, giggle
Sarah you menace
Are you sure you're not Dennis
Sorry Miss I can't stop
Because I've got the *g-g-g-giggles*
And the *w-w-w-wiggles.*

Sarah Harrison (11)
St Cuthbert's JMI School

BROKEN ARM

I remember when I was small
I trapped my arm in the door.
I went to the doctor to get a check
And it was broken in every speck.
I had some plaster on my arm.
That was not what I was wishing for.

John Tyson (10)
St Cuthbert's JMI School

THE TRACTOR

It's working all day
Making noises like *whoooo.*
The worst is when it's crushing things,
It sounds like a rusty robot that comes to life.
I always feel scared,
Like it's a monster that's after me.
I have dreams that it will come to life and kill me.

It's like a metal dinosaur.
Its claws are like jaws eating the ground,
Like it's a human body.
Its movement, like a roar,
Its tyres like gripping feet.
A sign says,
> *Danger*
> *Big Machines*
> *Beware!*

Daniel Tracey (11)
St Cuthbert's JMI School

SUNSHINE

The sun is shining, glistening in my eyes,
Daffodils in my garden,
Children running with glee,
Mothers sunbathing, reading books,
Tulips growing with happiness,
Neighbours being nosy in their garden,
Sun is laughing with a warm coat on.

Rebecca Doody (10)
St Cuthbert's JMI School

UNDER MY BED

I hear,
It's there.
It's got no hair.
It's scary, dark and bold.
I hear it's not very old.
I lie there all night thinking
It's going to jump up and give me a fright.
It eats my socks and gobbles my shoes.
I lie there listening to its laugh.
I snuggle up in bed trying not to think
But when I open my eyes, I see it blink.
I hug my ted and say I am safe.
I tell my mum,
She doesn't believe me.
But when I'm gone, all gobbled up,
She'll know.

Heather McCarthy (10)
St Cuthbert's JMI School

THE HAMSTER THAT BITES

I remember when I got my hamster,
It bit me deep inside.
I cried but then I nearly died
With the pain that went straight into my mind.
Then my mum got the doctor.
What a shock, she must have cried.
The doctor said 'I don't think we can
get her to come alive.'

Kirsty Taylor (10)
St Cuthbert's JMI School

PINS AND NEEDLES

Pins and needles they hurt so much
It's like you've got a frozen touch
You get pains in your fingers and pains in your toes
It lasts for a few hours and then it goes
It comes back soon
I'll tell you that
And when it comes back I'll have pains in the night
You wake up in a lot of pain
You cannot move
It's such shame
You turn on the telly to try and forget
But when you start thinking about it
You are dripping with sweat
Pins and needles they hurt so much
It's like you've got a frozen touch.

Symone Aryeetey (11)
St Cuthbert's JMI School

THE SLICKY WICKY MONSTER

The slicky wicky monster is nice
His back has spikes
And his curry has spice
He does not have many friends
But he collects pens
He is a good drawer
And a very loud snorer!
So if you do see a slicky wicky monster
Shout *Aaaaaaa!*

Peter Nodwell (11)
St Cuthbert's JMI School

THE DEAD OF NIGHT

Everything is dark
Everything is silent
In the dead of night

The wind whistles round the chimney pot.
Dogs bark in the distance
In the dead of night

Ghostly figures roam the streets
The moon shines through my curtains
In the dead of night

As it starts to get lighter
They go away.
I am glad it is no longer
The dead of night.

Rachael Bradley (11)
St Cuthbert's JMI School

MY RABBIT FLOPSEY

I have a rabbit called Flopsey,
And his ears are very floppy.
His fur is golden, white and brown.
He can jump up and down
And then he does the cutest frown.
I feed him on chopped carrots and cucumber.
How much food he's eaten - I've forgotten the number
And at the end of the day
He sleeps quietly in his hay.

Phoebe Dinn (9)
St Cuthbert's JMI School

I HATE . . .

I hate rain
I hate school
I hate hockey
I hate pool.

I hate books
I hate history
I hate English
I hate a story

I hate writing
I hate singing
I hate fighting
I hate soaps
I hate everything here!

David Morris (11)
St Cuthbert's JMI School

SUMMER

I love the sun
away from the rain
and play in the sun all day.
I love the sea-blue sky
and the summery red roses.
You could smell them even if you had tiny noses.
I love the springy green grass
and the pale white clouds.
To live in this world you should be proud.

Kathy Roche (10)
St Cuthbert's JMI School

THE GHOST OF CLASS 7

Shut the doors
Lock the windows
Pull down the blinds
Because no one is safe from the ghost of Class 7.
It crunches your bones then gobbles you up,
So don't move a muscle
And don't lift a cup.
Don't lift a finger,
Don't move a chair,
Because we all know that it's out there.
It scratches the blackboard
It goes through my ears
And when he goes
We end up in *tears*.

Katie Fox (10)
St Cuthbert's JMI School

THE MONSTER UNDER MY BED

At night I had a fright.
I heard noises and wondered
If it was Mum or the monster.
He's green and slimy
and scares me at night.
It lives under my bed.
My mother thinks I'm dreaming.
What if I am? But what if I'm not?
Will it eat me or will it not?
What if it wants friends?
I only worry when it's after me.

James Parry (11)
St Cuthbert's JMI School

AT NIGHT

Every night I creep up the stairs
and jump in my bed.
I hide under the blanket.
There is a voice calling to me -
'Jenny, Jenny.'
I think it's a monster
or a goblin trying to get me.
I think of a way to get out.
But the window is locked,
the door is shut and the lights are out.

What shall I do?

Jenny Melia (10)
St Cuthbert's JMI School

THE NIGHT SKY

Walking under the midnight sky breathless and motionless.
The moon is up and the sun is down.
The moon is dead.
The leaves blow into the midnight sky.
The wind blows through your hair.
The wind blows onto my face.
The leaves and the rain disappear onto the ground
As the rain hits the palm of my hand like a bullet shot out of a gun,
And the lightning's like a lion roaring in the circus.
The hailstones around all over the ground,
As the fog scatters all around on the ground.

Keil Patterson (10)
St Cuthbert's JMI School

THE BOXER

My favourite boxer is Mike Tyson.
He's wide as a pancake.
He is as strong as a brick wall.
He is as mad as a bull.
He is big as a house.
His muscles are like boulders.
He is as tricky as a fox.
He is famous like gold.
He is quick as lightning.
He is fearless as a shark.
He is a boxer like no other.

Luke Baker (10)
St Cuthbert's JMI School

GOING TO THE HEADMASTER

Oh no! Somebody's going to the headmaster
Creak! Creak! Down the noisy stairs.
As he bites his long nails in fright.
Down the quiet corridor,
All you can hear is the children outside playing happily.
I'd hate going to the headmaster but he's going right now!

Hannah Stanley (9)
St Laurence's RC School

A LIMERICK

There lived a Greek God called Zeus
Who loved to drink juice.
He said 'Hooray, I'll start my day
And then I'll play with my moose.'

Christopher Golding (8)
St Margaret Mary's Junior School

ME

When I'm angry it's like a volcano
About to erupt.
It's like bacon sizzling in the pan.
It's like a balloon about to explode.
But . . .
When I'm happy it's like a butterfly
Doing its own thing.

When I'm bored it's like a computer
With no games.
It's like a PlayStation never being fixed
It's like a room painted grey.
But . . .
When I'm happy it's like sunshine
On a summer's day.

When I'm scared it's like Scooby Doo
Going to solve mysteries.
It's like going on a roller-coaster
Without being strapped in.
It's like somebody tapping on my window.
But . . .
When I'm happy it's like
Easter everyday.

Jessica Lundberg (8)
St Margaret Mary's Junior School

THE PICNIC

This is what I heard my mum say,
'We're going to have a picnic.
Get up, wash your face, brush your teeth,
We have got to pack quick.

Hurry up . . . hurry up . . .
We're going to be late.
Oh no don't forget . . .
The dumb plate.'

When we got there,
We set the mat,
Oh man we have left,
Sam the cat.

Cake, sweets,
And other things.
Sausage roll,
And chocolate rings.

Half way through,
We made a mess
Do you know who made it?
Have a guess.

On the way back,
We had a crash.
Wham! Wallop!
Super bash.

Ryan J Beeley (8)
St Margaret Mary's Junior School

THE LADY OF SHALOTT

She stands in there,
The castle,
Dark,
With glitter underneath.
She watches the world appear
That shines so bright beneath,
She stays there in the castle,
She hasn't got a care.
She just sits there in the castle,
Weaving bright colours through her hair.
The tap on the door, the people say
Is the curse we know,
But when the curse is put on her
We know she'll have to go.
She has a mirror hanging there,
With all that she can see
When outside, but she does not know
A handsome man might be.
As she looks out of the window
Sir Lancelot trots by.
The curse upon her, sleepless,
The Lady of Shalott will die.

Kylie Windle (9)
St Margaret Mary's Junior School

THE BEST DAYS IN MY LIFE

The fluffy sheep were like fluffy clouds,
The old trees were like spiky fingers,
The steep hills were like large mounds of hay,
The small rocks were like stars sparkling in the sky.

Rachael Hawkins (9)
St Margaret Mary's Junior School

BOYS

Boys wear their hats backwards,
        Why?
They wear sunglasses
When it's not sunny,
        Why?
They come in covered in mud,
        Why?
They play with toy cars,
        Why?
They play on mountain bikes,
        Why?
They have girlfriends,
        Why?
They always get into fights,
        Why?
They play on skateboards,
And with Action Men,
        Why?
They always play football
And wear tracksuits
        Why?

Rebecca Achilles (10)
St Margaret Mary's Junior School

THE RECTANGLE WAS . . . ?

The rectangle was an exciting comic which every kid had read.
It was a heavy brick that was stuck in the house wall.
It was a beautiful picture frame that glittered when the light shone on it.
It was a deep swimming pool which I could swim in.
It was a massive window with a white window frame.

Danielle Davey (9)
St Margaret Mary's Junior School

THE BALLOON

B is for balloon way up high in the sky.
A is for air to keep you up flying high.
L is for loving it way up high in the sky.
L is for liking all the fresh air.
O is for orange, the colour of the sunset.
O is for orange that was made by the reds and yellows.
N is for night flying which I love best.

Faye Silvano (9)
St Margaret Mary's Junior School

THE RECTANGLE WAS . . .

It was a heavy brick that smashed the car window.
It was a delicious chocolate bar that the boy got all over him.
It was a comfy mat that everybody sat on.
It was a brilliant video that I was the star of.
It was a useful rubber that rubbed out spots.

Danielle Brennan (9)
St Margaret Mary's Junior School

PAN ROLLED OVER

There was a Greek God called Pan,
Who had a big van in Japan,
He rolled over and said,
'Oh I hurt my head.'
And that was the end of Pan.

David Jackson (7)
St Margaret Mary's Junior School

SUN AND MOON

The sun is a star,
The moon is magical,
Stars in the sky,
Sparkling at night,
Night and day,
Sparkling light.

Paula Bennett (10)
St Margaret Mary's Junior School

A GREEK GOD CALLED PAN

There was a Greek God called Pan,
Who got a nice suntan,
His son came and said
'Your face is all red,'
So, out of the sun he ran.

Helen Jennings (7)
St Margaret Mary's Junior School

A GOD CALLED PAN

There was a Greek God called Pan,
Who ran and ran and ran,
He was half man and half goat,
He got hot on his boat,
And so he bought a new fan.

Katy Walker (7)
St Margaret Mary's Junior School

THE RECTANGLE WAS . . . ?

The rectangle was a football pitch that Liverpool
                                   played and trained on all day.
It was a rubber that people rubbed out with all the time.
It was a window that was broken easily by a brick.
It was a red and brown brick that builders made houses out of.
It was a yellow piece of card that people drew or wrote on.

Scott Smith (9)
St Margaret Mary's Junior School

NO VEST PAN

There once was a God called Pan,
Who was half goat, half man,
He had a bare chest,
Never wore a vest,
And always topped up his tan.

Daniel Shelvey (7)
St Margaret Mary's Junior School

DEMETER'S DRINK

There was a Greek Goddess called Demeter
Who was just half a meter,
She took a drink,
And it was pink,
From the Happy Eater.

Laura Evans (7)
St Margaret Mary's Junior School

THE RECTANGLE WAS?

The rectangle was a smelly mat that a monster
                              wiped his feet on every day.
It was a horror video that everyone wanted.
It was a heavy brick that no one could lift.
It was a lovely glittery picture frame with a lovely picture of me in it.
It was a wooden door that I went through every day.

Steven Rourke (9)
St Margaret Mary's Junior School

SWALLOWING SEED

There was a Goddess called Demeter,
Who was going to the eater,
She then swallowed a pack
Of seeds off the rack,
And then ran back home to Peter.

Stacey Woodward (7)
St Margaret Mary's Junior School

PAN WITH THE SUNTAN

There was a Greek God called Pan,
Who went to Spain and got a suntan,
He was sheer red,
And went to bed,
And switched on his mini fan.

Liam O'Connor (8)
St Margaret Mary's Junior School

Boys!

Boys, boys make loads of noise,
Don't go to confession for weeks and weeks,
Don't go to choir 'cos they think it's for geeks,
They act really hard but they're really dead weak.

Boys, boys make loads of noise!

Lisa Price (9)
St Margaret Mary's Junior School

The Rectangle Was

The rectangle was a smelly mat that only the cat sat on.
It was a transparent window that you could see a hill through.
It was a brick that was too hard to carry.
It was a lovely picture frame that had glitter all over it.
It was a large table which had lovely patterns on it.

Michael Bennion (9)
St Margaret Mary's Junior School

The Rectangle Was?

It was a boring video that nobody wanted to watch.
It was a gigantic skyscraper that fell down ten days ago.
It was a massive swimming pool with no water in it.
It was a tiny playground that everybody played in.
It was a wide box with all my toys in.

Erin Knight (8)
St Margaret Mary's Junior School

THE RECTANGLE WAS . . . ?

It was a swampy football pitch that moved about
when players played on it.
It was a massive swimming pool and the water was deeper than the sea.
It was a mysterious notice board that everything disappeared off.
It was a great window because it didn't break.
It was a marvellous calendar because it had lots of patterns on it.

Erin Friel (9)
St Margaret Mary's Junior School

INSECTS

The insects that come out at night
they'll give you a terrible fright.
The slugs and the snails
oh yes they all leave trails
but I wouldn't fancy 'em for a bite.

Laura Harrild (10)
St Margaret Mary's Junior School

THE TIME OF MY LIFE

The small lambs were like a beautiful piece of silk,
The huge hills were like a *big* mountain of chocolate,
The green fields were like very soft material
that you could lie on forever,
The bouncy rabbits were like beautiful, bouncy fluff.

Emma Newnes (9)
St Margaret Mary's Junior School

SWEETS, SWEETS

My best sweets,
Fruit drops,
That sparkle like my eyes.

Cola bottles
Chew them, chomp them.

Jelly beans
Chewy crunchy colourful.

Lollipops,
Round and suckable,
Sticky and lickable.

Mints too
Hard ones, chewy ones
Soft ones, chocolate ones.

Gobstoppers,
Big ones, small ones
Rainbow colours
Changing all the while.

Carl James Wilkinson (9)
St Margaret Mary's Junior School

FEELINGS

The lady's sitting sad and stressed,
She is not happy, isn't feeling her best.
She's trapped in a castle by an evil curse,
Feeling like her heart may burst.
She is scared in case the curse is true,
She looks at her web wondering what she's to do.
She just keeps weaving, weaving, weaving.

Vicky Wynne (10)
St Margaret Mary's Junior School

PART 'S'

Roger never ever knew his dad
He'd never even been called a lad.
Buckets flew through the sky
And hit Cookee by his eye.
Then he got his memory back
And nearly broke his very sore neck.
But when he noticed his long lost wife
You could have stabbed him with a knife.
Who would have thought, who'd have knew
Well! It certainly fooled Ernestine, she went bright blue.
Even though Roger went bright red,
You'd have thought that someone had hit him on the head.

Suddenly there was a terrible *plopped squelch*
They walked on water with a *quelch*.
Someone could have knocked them down with a feather
You'd never have thought that Roger was actually very clever.
But now it's over
Everyone knows this great big secret I have told.

Lisa Ellison
St Margaret Mary's Junior School

MY MUM!

My mum is special everyone can see
How very much I love you and how much you mean to me.
You're there for me night and day mum,
You always seem to be the one,
Who helps me in good times, and in bad.
So my mum's great
And she's my best mate.

Cindy Meskell (10)
St Margaret Mary's Junior School

MY FAMILY

My family is weird,
As big as my beard.
My aunty's called Sue,
She got stuck in the loo.
My cousin's called Jen,
She's got a long pen.
My uncle's called Jack,
He's got a sore back.
My aunty's called Barb,
She won't let you starve.
My dad's called Col,
He bought me a rag doll.
My mum's called Maz,
Her brother's called Baz.
My aunty's called Ann,
She cooks with a frying pan.
That's them all,
So if you want them just call.

Nicola Sullivan (9)
St Margaret Mary's Junior School

SPACE

Space is a big place,
things floating in the universe,
planets are going round, round and round.
Astronauts finding out what space is like,
they float like a boat.
Comets are shining in your eyes.
Earth is our planet,
it is great like my mate.

Amie Boner (9)
St Margaret Mary's Junior School

JOLLY ROGER

Roger's mumsie nearly died, her heart was beating quickly,
As Cookee squelched onto the quay, his hair was wet and trickly.
'Yo, Ernestine!' he blurted out, 'I ain't seen you in years!'
The woman's eyes began to fill with little, twinkling tears.
Roger stood there still and froze, rooted to the ground,
He dropped his mouth and stood there gaping, without a single sound.
Roger's mum just stared at him and then began to smile,
I've got to say I haven't seen her do that in a while!
'Hallelujah!' shouted she, 'I'll never be alone!
For all these years,' she added on 'I've been all on my own.
But now,' she said, 'old Henry's back, I've never been so glad,
This is the best experience that I have ever had!'
Roger on the other hand was still remaining quiet,
The villagers were causing a tremendous, noisy riot.
He waited till the noise died down and then began to speak,
To Henry, Roger's father, who was very tired and weak.
'Daddy!' he exclaimed, 'I can't believe you're really Cookee!
Oh Dad, I've missed you loads, oh deary me, you're really mucky!'

James Dooley & Thomas McElroy (11)
St Margaret Mary's Junior School

MY BEST FRIEND

You're my best friend
But this is the end,
You're moving away
Today.
I hope I see you again
Because I have a pain.
So let's play
For the rest of the day.

Faye Mackereth (7)
St Margaret Mary's Junior School

DEATH COMES KNOCKING

The lady of Shalott
Sits in her castle
Singing a song.

A song that twists and turns
Through the dark halls
Until it comes to a stop.

And dark shadows come knocking on the door.

Should she open it?
Should she not?
Should she leave death knocking?

Out of the darkness came a shadow,
A shadow that she had never seen before.
It came after her.
She fell.
All you could hear was a scream.

Jenny Wright
St Margaret Mary's Junior School

MY PARROT

Look at my parrot,
Oh look at my parrot,
He is blue and green
Just like a marvellous tangerine.
It comes from an exotic island
In a tropical rainforest.
I don't have to take it back
Because it is mine
And it will always be mine.

Rachel Falshaw (10)
St Margaret Mary's Junior School

AT THE ZOO

When me and Jenny went down to the zoo,
We saw a dumb elephant, a big kangaroo,
A fast talking meerkat and a funny walking penguin too.

There was a gatekeeper eating a lovely cake
The lions roared which made us shake.

I saw a snake, it was slimy and thin,
And a rhinoceros, it looked tough.
I saw a sad woodpecker for the first time,
It had a long beak and shiny eyes.

I went to Sayers to buy a cake,
It was sugary so I gave it to Jenny Smith Lake.

Jenny said, 'Have you had a nice time?'
I said 'Yeah, I've had a great time all at Chester Zoo.'

Natalie Noon (8)
St Margaret Mary's Junior School

COLOMENDY

C is for Colomendy the greatest place on earth.
O is for orienteering that was fun.
L is for leaving school to go to Colomendy.
O is for outdoor games which were fun.
M is for Moel Fammau which was high.
E is for easy which some things were, extremely easy.
N is for nice which some people were, really nice.
D is for Devil's Gorge which was damp.
Y is for yes some people said when we were going home.

Michael Johnson (8)
St Margaret Mary's Junior School

HAMIE MY HAMSTER

H amie is my very cute hamster,
A nd all he does is sleep all day,
M y hamster is very cute when he first wakes up.
I n the night he goes in his wheel,
E very night he keeps me awake.

M y Hamie scampers across the room at 50 miles per hour,
Y ou'll be amazed at how fast he can run.

H amie is my first hamster
A nd he will probably be the last,
M y eyes can't stop looking at him,
S ometimes he climbs up my legs,
T oo much running makes him tired,
E very time he's tired he looks up at me,
R unning over to his cage and goes to sleep.

Danielle Jones (10)
St Margaret Mary's Junior School

MY HAMSTER

M y hamster's really nice,
Y ou always know when he's there.

H amsters are very cuddly,
A bit like a teddy bear.
M y hamster is quite fat,
S ometimes he goes in his ball.
T offey's his name,
E veryone likes him,
R unning around, he drives me up the wall.

Jennifer Kirby (9)
St Margaret Mary's Junior School

MINIBEASTS

Creepy crawly,
Guess what it is?
Slimy and slow,
Do you know?
It can hop,
It can fly,
It can climb up trees,
Have you guessed yet?
It can wiggle,
It can dance,
It can chirp,
It can buzz,
It can flutter,
What's that you mutter?
Yes it is a minibeast.

Charlotte Cuddy (9)
St Margaret Mary's Junior School

THE CASTLE

The castle standing high,
Turrets touch the sky.
Standing on an island
There below,
The river clearly flows
Down to Camelot.
Four walls surround
The castle proud,
Its grey, stone cloak
Wrapped all around.

Liam Ryan (9)
St Margaret Mary's Junior School

THE KNIGHT

She sees him pass,
A star at night.
She thinks,
'Is that my true-love knight?'
She looks at him, just like the sun,
Dazzling in the light,
Dressed in armour,
Plumes flowing from his helmet.
This is her chance,
But she is trapped.
She feels sad and blue,
There's nothing for her to do,
Except sit and wait for the day
She can leave.

Laura Quine (10)
St Margaret Mary's Junior School

WAITING

The castle is tall,
Has stone for its walls,
Dull, flat, grey on a cold winter's day.
Turrets at the top,
Where the stone walls stop.
Outside, some flowers,
Below, a barley crop.
She sits in the castle,
Hidden from sight,
Weaving alone, waiting for her knight.

Mark Seddon
St Margaret Mary's Junior School

MY FRIENDS!

My friends are really cool,
They are really good friends indeed,
Nicola is cool,
And Holly is funny,
Rachel laughs at everything,
And Kirsty is a nutter,
Kerry and Jessica are understanding,
And Katie is helpful,
All my friends are really great,
But one is quite special,
Her name is Lyndsey,
She is my best mate,
It's cool having friends you know,
Because that's what makes you great.

Sarah Edwards (9)
St Margaret Mary's Junior School

THE LADY OF SHALOTT

Dark in the dawn of Camelot,
A lonely woman weaves.
She sees the markets full of life,
While sitting alone, oh so blue,
Weaving through her life so glum,
She sees a dazzling light,
Shining through her crystal mirror.
There stands her true knight, looking above.
She wishes her life was somewhere else,
She is held prisoner by a curse.

Rachael Wright (10)
St Margaret Mary's Junior School

MY MUM

My mum is my best friend,
She is always there when you need a hand,
She is always there, with lots of care,
I really, really love her.

Sometimes she shouts or gives a yell,
'Quick, let's hide she's like a bat out of hell.'
She's calmed down now, let's give her a smile,
All is well, at least for a while.

She irons, cleans, and washes my clothes,
I think she needs a rest,
If you ever met my mum,
You would say she was the best.

Stephanie Wright (11)
St Margaret Mary's Junior School

SORRY!

Sorry if I hurt you.
Sorry if I made you cry.
Sorry I bumped into you.
Sorry I hurt your feelings.
Sorry I hurt you at all.

Sorry.

Sorry is only a small word
But to some sorry is the hardest word
They will ever have to say.

Nicola Carney (8)
St Margaret Mary's Junior School

HIGH ABOVE

In the castle, dark and cold
Rats and mice scamper
Across the stone floor.
High above in a room so small
A lady sits alone.
Click, click, click,
The only sound.
The sound of her needles
As she steadily weaves.
Thin, but beautiful
She does not look out,
She is trapped in the castle
Imprisoned by a curse.

David Roche (10)
St Margaret Mary's Junior School

WHY I LOVE MY MUM

I love my mum because:

She does the dishes,
She makes my wishes,

She gives me food,
Even when I'm rude,

She gives me clothes,
When I pose,

That is why I love my mum.

Nikita Marnell (11)
St Margaret Mary's Junior School

CURSED

The silent island of Shalott,
Rocky, spooky, dark,
But most of all home to someone everyone calls . . .
The Lady of Shalott.
She stays in one room,
Damp and dusty.
She does nothing, but weave night and day,
No one knows how she lives,
She does not eat, she does not drink.
All she sees are the shadows in her crystal mirror,
The curse is upon her . . .

The Lady of Shalott.

Alex Basnett (9)
St Margaret Mary's Junior School

ANIMALS

I love animals,
Dogs I always cuddle,
Some little puppies,
Sleep in a huddle.
I like going to the zoo,
I see animals and fishes too.
I sometimes go to the farm,
I see horses in a barn.
Animals, animals,
They are nice,
Little tiny ones,
Just like mice.

Anne Marie Barry (9)
St Margaret Mary's Junior School

MONSTER MADNESS

'Monsters' give me the creeps,
He doesn't eat cakes and sweets.

Instead he eats treacle
And lots of people.

'Monsters' never smiles
With one pace he can walk ten miles.

'Monsters' jumps on chairs and the settee
Cuts your hair and watches TV.

When he's got the flu,
He won't eat me or you.

Jennifer Mulcahey (8)
St Margaret Mary's Junior School

STAR, STAR

Star, star,
You sparkle like gold.

Star, star,
You sparkle like silver.

Star, star,
I see you in the sky.

Star, star,
You're next to the moon.

Hey star,
Can you see me on Earth?

Adam Clarke (9)
St Margaret Mary's Junior School

THUNDER

I am the god of wind,
My name is Thunder.
I make the wind change direction,
I make the football swerve,
I make the hurricanes fly.
People think I am cruel,
I say, *'Whoosh!'*
I do things that I want to do.
I am Thunder.
I blow the wind.
I am Thunder,
Whoosh!
I am the god of wind,
My name is Thunder.
I am the sound you hear in the night,
I am the creep that you hear.
People say I am scary,
I say *'Boo!'*
I am Thunder,
I blow the wind.
I am Thunder,
Whoosh!

Simon Eagles (10)
St Michael's RC Primary School

THE BEACH

I went to the beach and played in the sand.
The sun was shining and my skin got tanned.
The sea was blue and the seagulls flew overhead,
I found out I was dreaming and woke up in bed.

Neal Finnegan (9)
St Michael's RC Primary School

HOW MANY STARS?

When I was a girl
I would ask my mum
'How many stars are there hanging in the sky?'
'More than enough daughter,
more than I could say.
They'll keep you counting till your dying day.'

When I a girl
I would ask my mum
'How many fish are there swimming in the sea?'
'More than enough daughter,
more than I could say.
Enough to keep you counting till your dying day.'

When I was a girl
I would ask my mum
'How many creepy-crawlies are there?'
'More than enough daughter,
more than I could say.
Enough to keep you counting till your dying day.'

Emma Louise Thompson (8)
St Michael's RC Primary School

THE BUMBLE BEE

In a field of wondrous flowers,
A small bumble bee eats and devours.
If you scare him,
He will fly,
High, high, high into the sky.

Daniel Bromsgrove (9)
St Michael's RC Primary School

WIGGLY WORM

At the bottom of my garden lives a wiggly worm,
He's green, slimy and fat,
He lives on mud and leaves
And horrible things like that.

He lives at the bottom of my garden,
Where nobody goes and nobody knows,
But *me!*

He likes to wiggle and wiggle under the ground
And he likes to wiggle all around.
Sometimes I see him munching grass
This makes him move very *fast!*

He lives at the bottom of my garden,
Where nobody goes and nobody knows,
but *me!*

I call to see him every day
To see what he is having for tea.

Victoria Ward (8)
St Michael's RC Primary School

THE CLOWNS

Once upon a time there was a dizzy dizzy clown
who lived with his dizzy dizzy frown
and went to see his dizzy baby clown.
When he saw his dizzy baby clown
he went very dizzy dizzy.

Marnie Whelan (7)
St Michael's RC Primary School

WHY O WHY?

Fish swim
Birds fly
Dogs bark
But why o why?

Cats purr
Planes go high
Ducks quack
But why o why?

Horses trot
Babies cry
Lions roar
But why o why?

People talk
The rain goes dry
Frogs croak
But why o why?

Dean Wooding (8)
St Michael's RC Primary School

SUMMER

It's easy to tell that summertime's here,
The first sound of bees fills us with fear,
The flowers all open and show us their colours,
While children all want the paddling pool fuller,
The sun shines brightly up in the sky,
Then winter comes and we say 'Goodbye.'

Lauren Knight (10)
St Michael's RC Primary School

THE WORST WEEK OF MY LIFE

Monday was terrible I had too
many sweets and got bad teeth.

Tuesday was even worse I had
to go to my nan's and wash pans.

Wednesday was OK I suppose
but I got sick and broke my nose.

Thursday I got a yoghurt and
lost it in my pocket.

Friday I bought a frog and it
jumped round like a little dog.

Saturday I found a penny and
lost it in a bowl of jelly.

Sunday I had a bunny
next I had a jar of honey.

Laura Devaney (9)
St Michael's RC Primary School

BORING!

I am the god of nothing
My name is Boring
I do nothing because I am boring
Nobody likes me because I am boring.
My name is Boring
And I do nothing!

Adam Fletcher (9)
St Michael's RC Primary School

MY CAT

It purrs when it's happy,
It miaows when it's sad.
It climbs up the curtains,
And makes my mum mad.
All curled up and warm,
It sleeps in its box.
Awakes in the morning,
And plays with our socks.
It runs round in circles,
Until it's been fed,
It gets so exhausted,
It goes back to bed.
With a stretch and a yawn,
It walks off to its mat,
Goes back to sleep,
And this is my cat.

Siobhan Hughes (9)
St Michael's RC Primary School

COLOURS

C is for colours
O is for orange
L is for lemon
O is for over the rainbow
U is for underneath the rainbow
R is for rainbow
S is for smiling when the rainbow is out.

Jennifer Winstanley (10)
St Michael's RC Primary School

SPLASH

I am goddess of water
My name is Splash.
I make it rain on a sunny day
I breathe up water when people are
swimming so they can't swim.

My name is Splash
Goddess of water.

People think I am horrible
I say 'I don't care.'
I do more things that are horrible.

My name is Splash
Goddess of water
and I don't care.

Rebecca Finnegan (9)
St Michael's RC Primary School

THE SNAIL

The big slimy slithery snail,
Left a big slimy slithery trail.
Slowly sliding down the street,
Avoiding all the people he meets.
Its tentacles feel its food
until a bird comes and eats the
snail.

Lee Smith (10)
St Michael's RC Primary School

THE ZOO

I went out for the day,
a trip down to the zoo.
I saw elephants and tigers
and a bouncing kangaroo.

In the monkey house
there was a chimpanzee.
He was hanging and swinging,
high up in the tree.

'It's getting late,'
my mother said,
'It's time to go home
and go to bed.'

Andrew Boardman (9)
St Michael's RC Primary School

WHAT MY GRANDAD WAS LIKE

He was such a genial soul,
that is really true.

He took me out everywhere, even to the zoo.

He took me to the swimming baths,
he took me to the fair.

He took me to Scotland to see the *biggest* bear.

Robert Stranack (10)
St Michael's RC Primary School

PIRATES

Pirates are noisy, pirates are cruel,
they scare people off with their golden shoes.

The captain wears a hat with a skull and crossbones
and he always moans.

He has a parrot on his left shoulder and a wooden leg
and, to save your life, he wants you to beg.

He'll make you walk the plank and, down below,
lots of great sharks are smiling 'Hello'.

They'll gobble you up and eat you for lunch.
They'll bury bones for their small dog, Crunch.

Lyndsay Cave (10)
St Michael's RC Primary School

MY CAT

I've got a black cat,
Blacker than a black bat.
He's so fat he can't get off our mat.
His name is Kitty Kat.
He purrs while lying in the sun.
He miaows when playing and having fun.
He's mine and I love him so,
My little Kitty Kat with eyes that glow.

Craig Wallace (9)
St Michael's RC Primary School

MY SNOWMAN POEM

When Lucy woke she said '*Wow.*'
All on rooftops there was snow.
'I'm going to build a snowman.
It's going to be so high that it
will touch the sky.'
It was so high it nearly did touch the sky.
It was so high that at the end
she couldn't reach to put the eyes on,
and she couldn't put the nose on.
The next day there was sun.
'I shall feed him a hot cross bun.'
But when Lucy got out he was gone.

Heather Minghella (8)
St Michael's RC Primary School

A CAT

There is a cat in our street,
That has four little white feet,
Each night when I look out in the dark,
His eyes are shining like bright green sparks.
He lays on the cars enjoying the sun,
He always looks like he's having fun,
He has a tiny pink nose,
And when night comes he gets up and goes.

Jessica Large (7)
St Michael's RC Primary School

MY CHRISTMAS POEM

There was a rattle on the roof.
A creak in the corridors.
It was Christmas Eve so I knew,
it must be Santa Claus.
I heard him coming down the chimney.
He crept into the dining room,
he put the presents under the tree,
and shot back up with a *zoom*.
In the morning I woke up and
went straight down the stairs,
I opened all my presents,
and I knew that Santa cares.

Leanne Booth (7)
St Michael's RC Primary School

ME

I'm as quick as a cheetah
I'm as slow as a tortoise
I'm as funny as a clown
I'm as dull as a rainy day
I'm as tall as a giraffe
I'm as small as an ant
I'm as stupid as a dunce
And I'm as clever as Einstein.

Michael Napier (9)
St Michael's RC Primary School

THE GHOUL

Its eyes are like fire.
Its lips are ruby red.
Its fingernails can tear
through cotton and thread.
It eats children's hearts to obey his hunger.
When owls hoot the ghoul is near.
Children go missing out of sight,
parents find bones under their child's bed.
When people hear the owl
their lives are filled with fear.

The Ghoul.

Toni Doyle (9)
St Michael's RC Primary School

CRASH

I am the goddess of evil,
My name is Crash.
I leave fog and ice on roads,
I am Crash the goddess of evil.
The people think that I am very evil
When I am mad
I smile and say,
'Crash!'

Leah Kennerley (9)
St Michael's RC Primary School

MY BROTHER

My brother Paul he is rather small,
But one day I think he will be rather tall.
Because he's a brother he is a little bit of bother.
He climbs and he falls and sometimes he crawls.
He runs so fast and smiles and laughs.
He likes to play with blocks and he puts them in a box.
He growls like a tiger and plays with his toy spider.
Although he seems a menace he's a lovely little boy
and lots of fun and joy.

My brother Paul.

Katherine Tyson (8)
St Michael's RC Primary School

WICKED WILL

I am the god of evil,
My name is Wicked Will.
I make wheels skid,
I love crashed cars,
I love smashing windows.
People think I'm evil,
I say 'Bad luck!'
I do make people suffer.

Peter Collins (10)
St Michael's RC Primary School

THE BRILLIANT TWINS

The brilliant twins play and play
The brilliant twins like the day
The brilliant twins read a book
The brilliant twins like to cook
The brilliant twins like to write
The brilliant twins like the night
The brilliant twins go to school
The brilliant twins like to be cool
The brilliant twins have a brother
The brilliant twins have each other.

Clare Eagles (7)
St Michael's RC Primary School

EVIL

I am the god of evil,
My name is Crunch
I crash cars
I crunch cars up
I smash cars
People think I am evil
I say 'So what?'
I am Crunch
I crash cars.

Jenna Cleaver (9)
St Michael's RC Primary School

A BLACK CAT

A black cat sits on the window waiting for me to feed him.
One day I went out to him and scratched his neck
but he wanted me to feed him. I went in and said
'Mum, has my cat got a friend?'
She said, 'Yes, a black cat.
He sits on the window waiting for me to feed him.
I always go out and scratch his neck but he wants me to feed him!'
One day I got cat food and fed the black cat -
then he went off to another window.
That black cat's a greedy cat!

Kaydee Williams (7)
St Michael's RC Primary School

SUNSHINE

I am the goddess of sunshine,
My name is Bright.
I make it sunny when it rains,
I make it light at night.
People think I'm beautiful,
I say 'I'm just glad you're happy.'
I do nice things,
I am sunshine,
I am the sun goddess.

Christina Burrows (10)
St Michael's RC Primary School

RAINBOW

I am the goddess of rainbows,
My name is Colours.
I make colours,
I grant wishes,
I put a smile on everyone's face,
I play with the sun and rain.
People say I look good,
I say 'Thank you.'
I do all good,
I am the goddess of rainbows.

Lauren Gascoigne (10)
St Michael's RC Primary School

MY DOG

My dog will eat anything,
a cardboard box,
an old shoe lace,
a piece of cotton wool would do,
a newspaper is just the right thing,
and he tries to lick your face.
My dog will eat anything,
but do you know what my dog won't eat?
Dog food!

Katie Turner (9)
St Michael's RC Primary School

CRASH

I am the god of crashed cars.
My name is Crash.
I put ice on the roads.
I blow cars away
and I crunch them
then throw them away.
People think I am really mean.
I say I love crushing cars.
I am the god of crashed cars.
My name is Crash.

Michael Ormond (9)
St Michael's RC Primary School

BLUE

I like blue,
Blue is like the sea,
Every time I look at it, it shines upon me.

The waves shine and glisten,
The boats sail silently,
You can only hear a whisper
Of the nice cool breeze.

I like blue because I'm an Everton supporter!

Lois Taylor (10)
St Michael's RC Primary School

TRAVELLING

Cars are fast,
Cars are vast,
Cars go to everywhere.
Stop in London,
Visit big Ben,
Then come back to school again.

Trains are fast,
Trains are vast,
Trains go to everywhere.
Stop in Paris,
Get an ice-cream,
Then come back to Liverpool again.

Planes are fast,
Planes are vast,
Planes go to everywhere.
Stop in New Zealand,
Visit penguins,
Then come back to England again.

QiQi (9)
St Nicholas RC Primary School

POLLUTION

The world is full of pollution,
People throw rubbish about.
We have to sort out a solution
Before the world is wiped out!
Animals are disappearing fast,
If this goes on the world won't last.
Trees are destroyed day by day,
If we don't stop we will have to pay.

Hannah Edmondson (10)
St Nicholas RC Primary School

How I Found A Silver Pearl

As I climbed up a mountain
I saw two beautiful fountains
They were the most beautiful things
I'd ever seen
They looked like a King and a Queen
I saw a beautiful dove
Which to me was the sign of love
There were birds twittering
The fountains were glittering
I look down into the valley below
And I saw the river which made me quiver
As I looked up I saw the sky all blue
The clouds seemed like glue
Below the fountain I saw something bright
It was a faint little light
On a stone bathed by a streamy twirl
I found the silver pearl.

Vikram Aditya (10)
St Nicholas RC Primary School

Partytime

P arties, parties everywhere,
A nd presents are there too.
R ock and roll music
T o dance and listen to.
Y ou will be happy

T o organise a party
I n your own home, with your friends too.
M y party was full of bother,
E ven though I want another.

Tania Gerasimenko
St Nicholas RC Primary School

SUNSET WATERS

Sitting on the sand,
Watching the sun go down,
Sinking through the clouds.
I'm lying on the sand
With the sunset engulfing the water,
The water dances along slowly
While the sea creatures
Sing a sweet melody.
Slowly, slowly I fall asleep
Dreaming of sunset waters.

Jenna Doyle (10)
St Nicholas RC Primary School

THE GALAXY

The sun shines so brightly
When in the morning it's dawn
The moon looks so bright
When the night is dark.
The star which shines so brightly
With the day star and the pole star
That you can see.
I see the sun and the moon and the stars.
I like them all
And they belong to this world.

Lauren McNally (7)
St Peter's CE Primary School

SPACEMAN

Spaceman, spaceman,
as free as a bird.
I can float about,
I can jump,
I can roll.
It is great.
It's fun,
It's fuzzy,
It's the best.
I look at the Earth.

James Browne (6)
St Peter's CE Primary School

STARS

Stars in the bright sky
    Looking at me.
I smile up to them, and they
    Smile back at me.

Fiona Robinson (7)
St Peter's CE Primary School

THINGS IN SPACE

The sun is like a yellow jelly,
The moon is like a round basketball.
The earth has lots of green paper
On it for countries far and wide.
The stars sparkle like millions of
Tiny diamonds, sapphires, rubies and emeralds.
The comet speeds around like a giant bomb
From out of space with trickles of golden flames.

Rebecca Walmsley (7)
St Peter's CE Primary School

OUT IN SPACE

I feel as free as a bird,
I see stars like twinkling diamonds.
I see the moon like a great big football.
I feel dizzy when a comet spins round me.
I see strange, funny creatures on the moon
    that make me laugh.
I have a wonderful time.

Kenneth McCulloch (7)
St Peter's CE Primary School